Pocahontas
and Her World

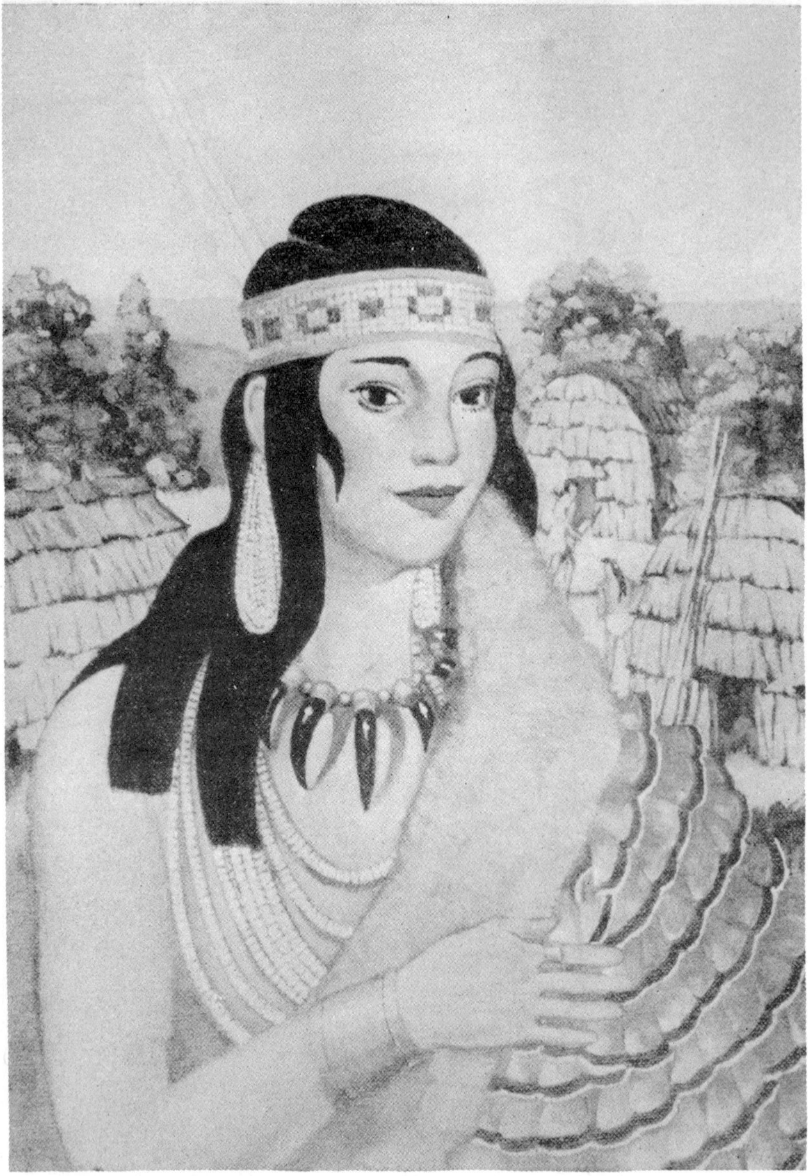

Pocahontas
AND
Her World

BY *Frances Carpenter*

ILLUSTRATED BY W. LANGDON KIHN

NEW YORK : ALFRED · A · KNOPF

L. C. catalog card number: 56-8905

© FRANCES CARPENTER HUNTINGTON, 1957

THIS IS A BORZOI BOOK,
PUBLISHED BY ALFRED A. KNOPF, INC.

COPYRIGHT 1957 BY FRANCES CARPENTER HUNTINGTON. All rights reserved. No part of this book may be reproduced in any form without permission in writing from the publisher, except by a reviewer who may quote brief passages and reproduce not more than three illustrations in a review to be printed in a magazine or newspaper. Manufactured in the United States of America. Pub-Distributed simultaneously in Canada by Random House of Canada, Limited, Toronto.

To my beloved Chip

The Reason for This Book

This is the story of a fearless young American who had a great deal to do with the founding of our country.

In all the history of the world, no other girl or boy has played a more heroic part in saving lives or stopping wars than the young Indian princess, Pocahontas. Her bravery is the reason for this book.

The world of Pocahontas was not like our world. Her America of more than three hundred years ago was not like the country we know. She did not know this land as "America." She had never heard the name "Virginia" given to the kingdom of her father, the great Powhatan. The river we call the "James" was, for her, the "Powhatan" or the "King's River." The York River, all along its course, was the "Pamunkey."

Before the strange Pale Face tribe came across the Great Waters to discover Virginia, Pocahontas and her people had never heard of writing or reading. So there are no Powhatan books to tell us just how she lived, what friends she had, and what things she liked to do.

Fortunately, her beloved "white brother," Captain John Smith, wrote a great deal about Pocahontas and her people. Other Englishmen who came with him in the "giant canoes with wings" also wrote about her wonderful world. They told of things they saw with their own eyes.

Because of their "True Reports," we can know what life was like in the America of Pocahontas. We can understand how important she herself was for each one of us in the America of today.

Contents

PART I
Her Wonderful World

Three Bears in a Wild Cherry Tree	3
Michabo's Magic	14
Running Fox Plays a Mean Trick	22
Visitors at Werowocomico	32
Nantakas Goes to War	41
The Mystery of the White Manitos	47
The Victory Dance	54
A Fight with a Fish	64
Brave Otter Makes Rain	71
The Feast of the Green Corn	82
The Great Deer Hunt	91
In the Time of the Co-honks	102

CONTENTS

PART II
New Friends and Foes

The White Strangers Come	113
An Okee Falls in Battle	123
A Wizard Is Captured	133
The Charm That Talked	141
Pocahontas of the Brave Heart	149
Blue Beads Save the Day	161
"Dear and Blessed Pocahontas"	170
A Dance for the Captain and a Crown for the King	180
A Messenger in the Dark	190
Captain John Smith Sails Away	202
A Princess Is Kidnapped	213
The Lady Rebekah and Master John Rolfe	223
A Strange New World	230
Books about Pocahontas and Her World	239

PART ONE

Her Wonderful World

Three Bears in a Wild Cherry Tree

THE bare brown feet of the Indian children were stained with red. It was the Month of the Strawberries, and the green carpet of the forest clearing was dotted with tiny berries. One could hardly take a step without crushing the juicy red fruit of the wild strawberry plants.

The fingers and lips of the children, too, were red. Half the sweet berries they picked were dropped into their mouths instead of into their baskets. There were plenty of wild strawberries for eating as well as for taking home to the village.

"Ho! Ho! Look at Pocahontas!" one of the children cried. "Pocahontas has painted her face well enough for a Corn Dance."

All the boys and girls gathered close to admire the

streaks of strawberry red on the girl's tawny cheeks.

"Strawberry juice is as good as red face paint made out of puccoon roots," said one of the boys. And the laughing children began to draw the juicy ripe strawberries across their own cheeks.

Pocahontas was laughing, too. She dearly loved fun, and she was usually the one who thought up the merriest tricks. This eleven-year-old girl was always the leader of the Indian children of the village of Werowocomico on the Pamunkey River.

It was not just because Pocahontas was the daughter of the great Powhatan, Chief-of-all-Chiefs of the Indian tribes along the Pamunkey and the Powhatan Rivers. It was well known, of course, that The Powhatan loved Pocahontas. Of all his many children, The Powhatan loved this small girl the best.

But everyone in that land loved Pocahontas. She was good to look upon, with her shining black hair and her sparkling dark eyes. Her love of fun and her gay ways made the place where she was always a happy place. It was easy to see why Powhatan had given her the nickname, Pocahontas, or Small-One-Who-Likes-to-Play.

The true name of Pocahontas was Matoax, which is to say "Little Snow Feather." But this name was seldom spoken outside her own family. These Indians believed it was safer so. For if some evil spirit should hear the girl's own true name, he might call her away and do her some harm.

The boys and girls of Werowocomico admired Pocahontas for the clever things she could do. She could outswim any other girl of her own age. She could climb a tree faster. She could walk longer on her two hands, with her feet high in the air. And, which was most unusual for an Indian girl, Pocahontas even could shoot rabbits and squirrels with her older brother's sharp arrows.

This day in the Month of the Strawberries was a day for tricks and for fun. The early summer sun was warm and pleasant on the children's bare bodies. Their Time of Cold was long gone by. No deerskins were needed now to keep them warm. Mantles of feather cloth would be far too hot.

The wild ducks and geese had already flown north again from their winter feeding grounds in the warm southland. By the thousands, the shad had swum in from the ocean and up the Great Salt Water Bay. They had laid their eggs in the still, fresh pools of the rivers of this part of America.

"When the oak leaves are as big as a ground-squirrel's ear, it is time to plant the corn." This is what the Werowocomico women used to say. And the corn had been planted. The trees in the forest were in full leaf.

"Remember! The biggest strawberries go into this basket for The Powhatan," Pocahontas reminded the other children.

The best of everything always was saved for the

Great King, her father. Like all the other Indians under his rule, the people of his own village never forgot their duty to Powhatan. To them, their Chief-of-Chiefs was almost as important as the Great Spirit who made their world. These Indian tribes of this part of America were called Powhatans; and far and wide, their mighty chief was known as *The* Powhatan.

The children had squatted down at their berry picking once more when, suddenly, they heard faint sounds far away down the forest path. Quickly, they raised their heads. They listened in silence. Then Pocahontas jumped up.

"It is Nantakas. I know his footsteps," she cried. And she ran off to meet this older brother of hers whom she loved so well.

The other children watched Pocahontas come with Nantakas back into the clearing. He was a fine fellow, this young son of The Powhatan. Tall and straight as a pine tree, he was. Handsome and young!

On this day, Nantakas was carrying a slender tree trunk over one shoulder. In his other hand was his sharp cutting stone. Round his neck hung a long cord made of thin strips of deer hide, twisted tightly together.

"What are you going to do, my brother?" Pocahontas was asking as they came near the others.

"I shall make a bear trap, little sister," Nantakas

replied. "I shall make a trap for those bears whose tracks we saw yesterday."

"Then I shall watch you." The Indian girl's eyes were bright with pride in her brave brother, who was afraid of no beasts, not even of bears.

Happily, Pocahontas ran ahead of Nantakas down the path that led into the forest on the other side of the clearing. They had gone deep, deep into the woods when suddenly she stopped short.

"Nantakas! Nantakas! You will not need a trap. Look! There! Up in the top of that wild cherry tree! One, two, three bears are there, eating the cherries."

Even in her excitement, Pocahontas did not forget to speak softly. Well did she know that a hunter must never let the beasts hear him.

Nantakas drew in a deep breath of astonishment. "*Ai-i-i,*" he said in a whisper. "Three bears in one tree! Who ever saw such a thing? And today I left my bow and arrows behind!"

"Run, little sister! Run fast! Fetch my bow and my arrows out of my wigwam."

The excited girl was gone almost before her brother had finished speaking. The sticks on the forest path snapped under her flying feet. Rabbits and squirrels and a red fox scampered deeper into the bushes. In one place a startled young deer lifted his short white tail and bounded off into the woods.

That deer ran no faster than Pocahontas. Her brother, Nantakas, did not have to wait long for his bow and his arrows.

The small black bears, still high up in the cherry tree, heard the racing feet of the girl coming back down the path. The animals pushed their pointed black noses out from under the leaves. Fearfully, they looked down on their two-legged enemies gathered below them.

In the forest, now, were many tawny, brown bodies. All the strawberry pickers had come running to see what Nantakas was doing.

Several young men had followed Pocahontas out from the village. They, too, had brought their bows and their arrows. But, of course, the three bears in the cherry tree were for Nantakas to shoot.

Fitting his first arrow to his bowstring, Nantakas took aim at the black bear on the lowest branch. He pulled the string back, back. Then he let it go.

"Zing-ng-ng!" His arrow sped to its mark.

"My brother's arrows have eyes that see the way clearly," Pocahontas cried as the small black bear tumbled, dead, out of the tree.

A second arrow was fitted to Nantakas's bowstring. It, too, found its mark. The second black bear was killed. Everyone shouted then, "Good! Good! Truly, Nantakas has arrows with eyes."

Now there was just the third and highest bear left

"Three bears in one cherry tree! Whoever saw such a thing?"

Three Bears in a Wild Cherry Tree

in the cherry tree. This one was almost hidden from sight amid the leaves of the treetop. Nantakas could not see the part of the bear's body which he wanted to hit. But he sent his arrow flying up toward its black shape amid the green leaves.

This third bear was not killed at once, as the two others were. The Indian's arrow pierced only the hind leg of the beast. But this made the bear lose his hold on the high tree branch. Down, down, the bear fell.

The animal landed on the hard earth with a great thud. And the fall broke his back.

At the sound of his loud cries of pain, Pocahontas felt sorry for the poor beast.

"Kill the bear, Nantakas! Kill the poor creature quickly," the soft-hearted girl cried.

"No! That I'll not do!" Nantakas replied fiercely. "This bear is a coward. He does not die bravely."

Then he spoke to the bear as if that wild creature could understand his Indian words.

"Bear! O, Bear! Are you so weak that you scream like an old woman? Do you not know that the Great Spirit, Manito, made you for the use of men like me? Man and bear, we are meant to fight one another. This time you have lost the fight. Are you a baby, or an old woman, that you cannot bear your pain bravely?"

Suddenly, Pocahontas did not feel so sorry for the wounded bear. Like all her people, she did not like a coward. It was a disgrace, she knew well, to cry out for pain.

Had she not seen Nantakas once hold a stone, hot from the fire, in the palm of his hand? She was proud that her brother had not made any sign that he felt its sharp burning pain.

The bravery of every Powhatan boy was put to the test. He must run between long lines of men who beat him with sticks. And he must not cry out.

Pocahontas herself, when only a very small girl, had not shed one tear when her ears were made ready for her first earrings. The sharp pointed splinter of bone had hurt when it made the holes in her ears. And the greased strings her mother pulled through the holes to keep them well open until they were healed! Oh, those had hurt, too. But she had not cried.

Truly this black bear was a great coward. He did not deserve pity. Yet she was glad when Nantakas, at last, put an end to his cries with another arrow.

When Nantakas and his friends brought the bears back to the village, Pocahontas shouted along with the other boys and girls, *"Woo-oo-woo! Woo-oo-woo!"* This was to tell the women that the hunting had been good. Many hands would be needed to take the skins off the bears and cut up their meat.

There was rejoicing in Werowocomico at the sight of the three bears. Even after the hearts and the livers were given to The Powhatan, even after an offering had been made to the Great Spirit, there would be fresh meat for all.

There would be much bear grease, too. These black bears were plump. They must have scooped many shad up out of the rivers. They must have found many berries and much fruit, as well as plenty of roots, to eat in the forest.

Pocahontas and the other girls would help their mothers to boil the fat parts of the bear meat in the stone cooking pots. With wood ladles, they would skim the cooled grease off the top. Then, they would put it safely away in the heavy skin grease bags.

The bear grease would be kept to season their food. It would be useful, too, for oiling their bodies to keep the biting gnats and mosquitoes away. Bear grease, mixed with the powdered roots called puccoon, made their precious red body paint.

Of all the wild animals, except the deer, none was more useful to Pocahontas and her people than these small black bears. They roamed through the woods and the swamps of her land. But it was seldom that as many as three bears were found up in one tree.

That is why Nantakas, that night, made a song about his good hunting. That is why he was always so proud of the fine necklace he made from the claws of these three bears in the wild cherry tree.

she cried. And she threw several red berries up into the air.

A bluebird darted down from a branch over her head as the berries fell to the ground.

"Perhaps the bluebird will carry a berry all the way to Manito's wigwam beyond the sun." The girl's eyes followed the swift flight of the bird up into the treetop.

Manito, the Great Spirit, was seldom forgotten by these Powhatan Indians. For them, all the spirits of their land were important. But Manito was most important of all.

Pocahontas believed there were, all about her, good spirits and bad spirits. The trees and the flowers, the beasts and the birds—all these had spirits! Of this she was sure.

There were the good spirits in the sun, in the moon, and in the stars. But there were many bad spirits, too.

Bad spirits rode with the storms. Their voices were in the thunder. They sent the fire of the lightning down out of the clouds.

The temples of wood and bark near the villages of this land were the homes of Okeus, chief of all the bad spirits. In them the Indians kept the strange idols which they called their Okees. Always, they took their Okees with them into battle to frighten their enemies.

"For thee, Okeus!" Pocahontas threw a few more

Michabo's Magic

strawberries in the direction of the temple in the forest beyond the Werowocomico wigwams.

One must take care not to neglect this cruel god. Okeus would be quick to punish anyone who forgot him. It was Okeus, the Evil One, whom these Indians feared. It was Manito, the Good and Great Spirit, whom they worshipped and loved.

"The Great Spirit, Manito, is the maker of all things," Powhatan reminded Pocahontas. "Manito made this good land of ours. He gave it to us for our home. In its waters he placed all the creatures that swim. On the sandy floor of our Great Salt Water Bay, he laid down clams, oysters, and crabs for us to eat.

"In our forests Manito put the land creatures which also give us food. The animals that walk on four legs! The animals that creep on the ground! The animals that fly! The animals that swim! All these living things the good Manito made for us to use."

"Tell me again, my father, how it was when the Great Spirit first made our world." Pocahontas settled herself more comfortably on the grass mat.

"Who knows how it really was, my dear daughter?" Powhatan put another red strawberry into his mouth. "My father told me it happened long, long ago when the Great Spirit once took on the form of a hare. An enormous white hare he was. Michabo, the Great White One, was his name then. Some say that name only meant Great White Hare. Others say it meant instead The-One-Who-Gives-Light.

"Whichever it was, our forefathers said it was Michabo who made the world. First he made the Great Salt Waters, the ocean. Then he made the land that floats upon them. My father always said Michabo made our land from one grain of sand which he took from the bottom of the great sea.

"When Michabo breathed his magic upon it, the grain of sand grew bigger. It grew and it grew. At last it grew into such a big land that the swiftest deer could not run across it in all the years of his life.

"The Great White One threw the sun, the moon, and the stars up into the sky. He made other gods, too. Among these were the four spirits who ride on the winds. One cannot see these wind gods as one can see fire and water. But one can feel them as soon as they come forth from their wigwams at the four ends of the earth.

"Michabo next made men and women. To keep these people safe until he could make animals for their food, the Great White One shut them up inside a huge bag.

"Michabo had finished making the very first deer. Then for some reason or other, he had to go back to his wigwam up in the sky.

"It was while he was gone that the four wind gods

Michabo's Magic

came along. They killed Michabo's deer. And they ate up every little bit of its meat. They left only its skin behind when they flew off to their wigwams at the four ends of the world.

"Michabo was angry. 'I will make more than one deer next time,' he said to himself. 'I will make so many deer that not even the four wind gods can kill them all. My people shall always have deer meat for their food. They shall always have deerskins for their clothes.'

"The Great White One plucked thousands of hairs off the deerskin. He scattered them far and wide over the earth. By his great magic, each one of those thousands of hairs turned into a deer that bounded away into the woods. From them have come the deer which our hunters bring home from the forest today.

"With so many deer, there was meat in plenty for Michabo's people." Powhatan wiped his damp strawberry-stained fingers on the grass mat beneath him. "So the Great White One opened the bag and let his people come forth into the light. And he taught them how to live in the good land he had made for them.

"Michabo showed men how to make their wigwam frames from straight young tree trunks. He taught them to lay great pieces of tree bark, or mats made of reeds, over the wigwam frames so the wind and rain could not get in.

"The Great White One told his people to take fish from the rivers, and oysters and crabs from the ocean floor. Above all these things he taught the men how to hunt in the forests.

"Even now, when we seek a new hunting ground, we ask Michabo to help us. Often and often the Great White Hare has come to me in a dream. Leaping before me, he has shown me the way to a forest filled with fat deer.

"It was the Great White One, too, Pocahontas, who put the fruits and the nuts on the trees. He planted the first corn and he told the women how to tend it. He gave us beans, melons, and pumpkins to eat, and tobacco leaves to dry and smoke in our pipes.

"It is Manito who makes all things to live. And when we have lived long enough, surely it is Manito who sets our feet on the path to his Land of the Sky. That is a shining path, edged with sweet berries like these you have brought me. Aye, Manito's Sky Country is a happy land where there is a feast every day."

"But why, O why, my father, did Manito make such a cruel god as Okeus?" Pocahontas always whispered when she spoke of this Evil One.

"Who knows that either, Little Snow Feather?" Powhatan shook his gray head. "All we know is that this Okeus has strong magic, too. We know he is quick to punish those who make him angry. He sends the sickness that takes away our strength. He keeps rain from falling on our corn fields. He hides the deer from our sight. We only can try to keep Okeus contented so that he shall not spoil our good gifts from Manito."

hatan's young wives and children who dwelt under the arching bark roof of his long house.

Powhatan had houses in many of the towns of his broad kingdom along the Great Salt Water Bay, the Chesapeake. A mighty chief such as he must have many wives to tend his wigwams. Many were needed to work in his corn fields. It took many hands to cook for his guests and to make his mantles of deerskin, feather-cloth, and fur.

On this summer morning, the Pamunkey River shone like bright metal under the rays of the sun. The children made rainbow splashes as they dived into its cool waters. Like young otters, they swam and played, in and out of the stream.

It was Pocahontas who first spied the small log canoe coming out from the river bank.

"It is Running Fox! In his father's new canoe!" she cried out. Running Fox was her cousin, but sometimes Pocahontas did not like him very well. Running Fox was too fond of teasing, she thought. Often the tricks he played made the other children unhappy.

The small log canoe came on and on. With swift strokes of his paddle, Running Fox sent it straight towards the swimmers.

When he was close beside them, the boy laid his paddle across the bow of his boat. He bent down and lifted up a long stick from the boat's bottom. Across it there hung an enormous dark-colored snake.

Running Fox Plays a Mean Trick

"A snake! A snake! Running Fox has a live snake!" the children cried in excitement. And just at that moment, Running Fox flung the long dark snake into the water.

"It's a white-mouth!" he called. "You'd better get away fast."

"A white-mouth! A white-mouth!" With squeals and loud cries, the frightened children swam for the river bank.

Who was not afraid of this deadly gray-black snake with its mouth lined with white? The white-mouth's bite was as much to be feared as that of Grandfather Rattlesnake, or the copperhead, his cousin.

The frightened boys and girls did not have time to think that Running Fox would never have put such a poisonous snake into his boat.

"Ho! Ho!" Running Fox laughed and laughed as he stood there in his log boat. "What brave ones you are!" he teased. "That was no white-mouth. It was only a black snake."

As if to prove he spoke truly, the long black snake wriggled out of the river onto the bank. All could see now that it was indeed only a common black snake. And these Indian boys and girls knew very well that the black snake does not have deadly fangs like the poisonous moccasin with the white mouth.

Pocahontas did not laugh with Running Fox. Instead, she dived into the river again. "Come with me!

Come!" she shouted to the other children as she disappeared under the water.

When she came up again, Pocahontas was at the side of Running Fox's canoe. Before he knew what she was doing, she had snatched away the paddle that lay across the bow of his boat.

"Now let us see how you will get to shore, Running Fox!" the girl cried.

Pocahontas pushed against one end of his canoe, and the little log boat began to turn around in the swift river. Other children swam to help her. And they pushed Running Fox's log canoe far, far out into the middle of the deep stream.

A boy in a boat without a paddle is indeed in bad trouble. Running Fox did not dare to dive from the boat to go after his paddle. He knew that the river might carry his father's canoe far out onto the great waters of the Chesapeake Bay.

"I will be good! I will not play that trick again!" the boy promised. At last Pocahontas brought his paddle back to him. And the swimming children helped Running Fox get his boat to the shore.

As usual, after their morning swim in the river, these young Indians were hungry. They raced back to their wigwams, and the warm summer sun dried the drops of water that stood up on their well-oiled skins.

Running Fox Plays a Mean Trick

Corn cakes and boiled beans and a stew of deer meat were waiting for Pocahontas.

"We are weeding the corn fields today," the girl's mother said as soon as the breakfast was eaten. "Will you help weed, Little Snow Feather? Or will you take your turn on the watching-platform?"

"First I will weed. Then I will watch over the corn," Pocahontas decided.

She liked to work with the women in the corn fields beyond the wigwams. Among her people, tending the green plants which Manito gave them for food was woman's work. It was man's work to hunt and to fish and to fight off their enemies.

The green corn plants were now higher than the girl's waist. Beans were growing between the cornstalks. Pumpkin vines ran over the ground below them. But there were weeds as well. These had to be pulled out if the corn was to grow well.

The women talked as they worked amid the corn. Sometimes they told stories. The children all liked to hear them.

Even while the women were in the corn fields, watchers were needed to keep birds and beasts away. Rabbits and skunks and many other four-footed creatures liked the sweet taste of the green cornstalks. Now and then, the boys and girls on the high watching-platform would see the fat brown form of a woodchuck creeping close to the ground on its short little legs.

With loud cries, the children would jump down and chase the woodchuck away. Or, if one of the boys had his bow and arrows with him, the others would keep very still. An arrow might kill this robber in their corn field. Then the young hunter would have woodchuck stew for his supper.

On this day, Pocahontas had brought her newest pet with her to the corn-watching-platform. It was a little raccoon which Nantakas had found for her in the forest.

The girl loved this pet, with its soft furry gray body, its sharp little nose, and its bright eyes rimmed with black fur. The tiny coon was still very young, but already it would eat an earthworm out of her hand.

Pocahontas had tied a deerskin cord around the leg of her little coon. A stick at the other end of the cord was pushed into the ground on the edge of the corn patch. The Indian girl could look down and see her pet playing there.

She was watching the corn field when one of the other children called out, "Pocahontas! Your coon! A great horned owl has flown off with your baby coon."

Like lightning, the great horned owl had swooped

Running Fox Plays a Mean Trick

down out of the sky. With its strong claws, it had grabbed up the little raccoon. It had lifted it, along with the stick on the cord, high off the ground. Before Pocahontas could jump down from the platform, the owl had flown off with her pet to a tall walnut tree on the edge of the field.

Running Fox, too, had seen the great horned owl. The boy had been standing alone, a little distance away. Since that morning the other boys and girls had not been talking to him.

Running Fox must have been sorry for his mean trick. For now he ran like a deer across to the walnut tree where the horned owl had her nest. The other children ran, too, but Running Fox was there first. And swiftly, like a squirrel, he began to climb up the tall tree.

"Take care, Running Fox!" Pocahontas called out. "Take care! The horned owl has a wicked beak."

But the boy climbed and climbed.

At last he was sitting astride a branch just above the hole in the tree trunk where the horned owl had her nest. He could look in and see three little owls. It was for her children's supper that the mother owl had snatched up the wee raccoon.

The mother owl herself was now perched on a limb of the tree above the head of the boy. The baby coon had been dropped on a tree branch just below her.

Running Fox was reaching up for the coon, when

the great owl flew down at him. Her strong wings beat against his head. Her splinter-sharp beak pecked at his shoulder. And the blood came.

The boy did not cry out. With his fists, he bravely struck out at the angry mother owl until he drove her away.

With the tiny coon tightly tucked under one arm, Running Fox climbed down the tree. His head was a

"Take care, Running Fox! The horned owl has a wicked beak."

Running Fox Plays a Mean Trick

tangle of long black hair, leaves, and twigs. His shoulder was bleeding, but there was a smile on his face. Gently, he put her pet, safe and sound, into the hands of Pocahontas.

"Running Fox truly is good again," Pocahontas said, praising him.

"Running Fox is good again," the children all nodded their heads. Because of the boy's brave battle with the great horned owl, he was forgiven for the mean trick he had played with the black snake that morning.

Visitors at Werowocomico

"THEY come! The weroances are here!" Pocahontas called down from her lookout in a tall tree on the river bank.

"Good! It is the time." The Powhatan spoke from his seat on a reed mat on the ground at the foot of the tree.

"Weroance" was the Powhatan name for a chief. And Werowocomico, the name of Powhatan's town on the Pamunkey River, meant "Town of the Great Chief."

Thirty and more tribes, under thirty and more weroances, were joined together under The Great Powhatan. In the towns all along this part of the Great Salt Water Bay, more than eight thousand Indians called him their Great Weroance.

"How many boats do you see, my daughter?" asked this Weroance-of-Weroances.

"Two canoes coming near, I see." Pocahontas shaded her eyes with her hand. "And there are two other canoes at the far bend of the river."

"Aye, four is the number," Powhatan spoke to his son, Nantakas, who squatted beside him.

Pocahontas had heard much talk about the meeting of these weroances with The Powhatan. She knew it had to do with an unfriendly tribe that lived to the west of her father's country. She shivered a little whenever she thought of those wicked people.

"The men of that tribe are not people of our Powhatan wigwams," her father had said. "In the dark of the night, they creep into our Powhatan villages. They steal from our people's corncribs. When our men are away from home, hunting the deer, those strangers carry their women and their children away."

Pocahontas was glad her sleeping mat was spread in the wigwam of The Powhatan. Four strong men stood always on guard outside. One was at each corner, all the night through. Sometimes Pocahontas waked when they shouted, one to the other. She listened to be sure they were giving the Indian call that meant "All is well."

Six sleeps ago the bad news had come. A runner,

sent by one of these four weroances, had brought the tale. He had told how two young Powhatan hunters, Red Cloud and Great Turtle, were out on a hunting trip. How an enemy band from the west crept through the woods in the dark of the night to steal the deer they had taken! And how this band of unfriendly men killed the two young hunters, even while they were asleep!

"We will teach that tribe to stay in their own part of the land," Powhatan had said when this tale was told. And he sent off his runners to summon the four weroances whose wigwams were nearest this enemy.

When the four boats came to land, Powhatan was standing in the midst of his men, waiting to welcome his guests. The old Chief made a fine figure. On this summer day, his bronzed body was bare, except for the strip of very soft deerskin which covered his middle.

With its rubbing of bear's grease, his tanned skin shone in the sun. Necklaces of copper and pearls, strings of fine shells and bears' teeth hung round his neck. Glistening white shells swung from his ears. Streaks of red and white paint ran across his tawny cheeks.

The old man's gray head, with its proud eagle feathers, was held high, as a king's head should be.

"We have come, Wahunsonacock." The weroances used the Chief's own name instead of his tribal title, The Powhatan.

Visitors at Werowocomico

"It is good, my brothers, I make you welcome." Powhatan motioned to them to sit down on the reed mats spread opposite his own.

Young men who had come with the weroances brought gifts for The Powhatan out of their big log canoes. There were brown bundles of deerskins and otterskins. There were pearls which they had found in the shells of oysters and mussels from Chesapeake Bay's bottom.

"Wingan! Winganouse! (Good! Very good!)" Powhatan's dark eyes shone with pleasure when these treasures were spread before him. All the tribes under his rule had to make such gifts to their Great Weroance. Each year they must bring corn for his winter eating, and rich presents to fill his treasure house.

When the welcome ceremony was over, Powhatan rose. He led the way to his wigwam where his wives had made ready a feast for the guests.

Powhatan took his seat on his own broad sleeping couch at the end of the huge room. Sitting mats were in place, ready for the visitors. Pocahontas brought a bowl of water so that they might wash their hands before they ate. And her mother brought bunches of soft turkey feathers with which to dry them.

It made Pocahontas hungry just to smell the roast turkey and deer meat. She longed to take a taste of the baked fish and steamed crabs. But even when there were no guests in the wigwams, Indian women and girls always waited until the men had eaten their fill.

The wooden platters of food went around again and again. At last Powhatan and his guests could eat no more. With sighs of content, they settled themselves more comfortably on their reed sitting mats. In silence, they waited for their Great Chief to speak.

"Now they will light the red pipe!" Pocahontas whispered to the other children who had crept into the wigwam to watch and to listen.

One of Powhatan's wives brought him a small bundle. The old Chief took off its cover of soft cream-colored deerskin. Carefully he lifted up a long, long pipe. Its smooth bowl was carved out of a reddish-brown stone.

Powhatan held the pipe high. All could see its fine trimmings of red feathers and white porcupine quills.

"Look! Wahunsonacock is lighting the red pipe," one of the children whispered to Pocahontas. They watched as The Powhatan laid a red-hot bit of wood upon the tobacco inside the pipe's bowl. They stood quiet and still as he took his first puff of smoke.

Then Powhatan put the glowing pipe into the hands of the weroance nearest him. From one hand to another, the red pipe traveled about the circle of men. Each weroance took just one puff of smoke, then passed the pipe on.

Last of all, the red pipe was given to Thunder

Eagle. This old Indian was the wisest medicine man in Powhatan's land. Thunder Eagle declared he often talked with the spirits. His strong magic, he said, came from the splendid dreams which the spirits sent him in his sleep.

With his songs and his dances, Thunder Eagle's magic could make sick people well, so these Indians believed. Perhaps that is why they called such magic "medicine." Perhaps that is why people like Thunder Eagle were called "medicine men."

This old medicine man also could foretell things that were to happen. So he always was given a place of honor in The Powhatan's Council Circle.

"Brothers!" The Powhatan began to speak when the red pipe had been smoked. "Brothers, our neighbors to the west have forgotten the time when their forefathers took our forefathers' hands and swore to be our brothers. They now are our enemies.

"My brothers, dark clouds cover the western sky. Those who live there under the setting sun have killed our brave warriors, Red Cloud and Great Turtle. They have taken their scalps. This wrong they must pay for. A kill for a kill! A scalp for a scalp! So it was with our grandfathers. So it is with us!"

"Wingan! Wingan! (Good! Good!)" All the people who had crowded into the great wigwam to listen, shouted that The Powhatan spoke good words.

Peace with their friends! War with their enemies! This was the law by which people lived in America in those times.

Powhatan turned to the old medicine man, Thunder Eagle.

"Grandfather," he cried, "Give us of your medicine! Is the time right for our warriors to go into the west? Will the spirits give them the victory?"

Thunder Eagle rose. As he stepped into the center of the Council Circle, he was fearful to look upon. His face was painted red, black, and white. From his headband there hung the skins of ten rattlesnakes. The snakeskins were stuffed with moss. And as the old man moved, their dry rattles talked as loud as if the snakes were alive.

Thunder Eagle also was wearing skins of many weasels, those fierce little beasts who do not fear to fight animals three times their own size. A rattle, made of a dry gourd with pebbles inside, was held in his left hand. His medicine spear was raised high in his right hand.

Pocahontas and the other children moved closer together when the old medicine man began to sing his magic songs. They trembled a little as he began his slow dance on the earth floor of the wigwam.

The songs of Thunder Eagle saluted first the good Manito, then the fierce Okeus, then the other spirits from whom he asked help.

Visitors at Werowocomico

*"A strong wind blows from the West.
A great storm comes from the West.*

*"But eagles do not fear the strong winds.
Eagles do not fear the great storm.*

*"Manito, look down upon us!
Okeus, fight on our side."*

Again and again, Thunder Eagle sang his wild song. He stamped on the ground. He crouched, and he leaped in his medicine dance.

Then, all at once, he stood still.

"It is good, Wahunsonacock!" he cried. "The spirits have spoken into my ear. Many scalps will be taken by Powhatan braves."

The excited crowd in the wigwam now began to shout.

The men and boys patted their open mouths as they gave their battle cry, *"Ow-ow-ow-ow! Ow-ow-ow-ow!"* Pocahontas joined in. She rattled her tongue between her parted lips while she made the shrill sounds of the Indian woman's war cry.

That night the war drums beat in Werowocomico. The war dance went on far into the night.

Around and around a tall painted post, the men leaped in their dance. They shouted as they looked up at the scalps from other wars, which floated from the top of the post. With their tomahawks raised, they jumped at this post as if it were a live enemy.

Next morning the four weroances hurried home in their canoes. Runners were sent out to all the villages in the western parts of Powhatan's country.

Young men there felt the taps of the runners' sticks on their bare shoulders. These told them that their king, The Powhatan, had declared war on the enemy tribe whose members had killed Red Cloud and Great Turtle.

A war party from Werowocomico would come to fight beside them. This, the runners promised. When the time came for the attack, many Powhatan warriors would set forth together. With their bows and arrows, their war clubs, and their stone sharp-edged tomahawks, they surely would crush these western foes.

Nantakas Goes to War

"Do not go, Nantakas! O, do not go this time, my brother!" Pocahontas was pleading. "Let the older braves ride forth in the war canoes. I need you here to protect me."

The tall young man was putting his arrows into the deerskin case which hung at his side. His face and his body were already painted with the black, white, and red colors of war. One half of his tawny face was red. The other half was black and white. He looked very fierce.

"Would you have me a coward, little sister?" he asked. "No, you would not have Nantakas stay home like an old woman, while the others go forth to punish our enemies. You shall fetch me my birdskin charm out of my wigwam. It will help me to fight well. It will help me bring back many enemy scalps."

As she ran on her errand, Pocahontas felt ashamed of the silly words she had spoken. Of course she did not want her brother to be a coward.

"Here is the birdskin charm, Nantakas," Pocahontas was smiling now. This charm was good medicine. The skin of the gray kingbird, which fought so fiercely with bigger birds, surely had magic.

And besides, this special kingbird skin was stuffed with sharp weasel claws. For Nantakas, the weasel claws would be the best medicine of all. Spirits had told him that, once, in a dream.

When she hung the birdskin charm around his neck, Pocahontas recalled her brother's strange dream. The dream was a great secret. If it was talked about, it might well lose its magic power. But Pocahontas had once heard Nantakas tell it to The Powhatan.

Her brother's secret dream had come to him when he was no older than she. In his dream he had been alone in the deep forest. Night had come, and he had curled himself up to sleep under a tree. Then, all at once, a huge black bear had appeared.

O, that bear in Nantakas's dream was four times as big as any bear ever seen. And its great paws were reaching out for the frightened boy.

The bear was just lifting Nantakas up off the ground when a little brown weasel ran out of a hole in the tree. Before the boy's eyes, that little brown weasel seemed to grow larger. It grew and it grew. If the black bear was big, this weasel was even bigger.

In his dream, Nantakas told The Powhatan, the great weasel jumped up on the bear's back. It bit and it clawed. It fought the bear so fiercely that the beast dropped the boy and ran off into the woods.

So, in his dream, it was a weasel that saved Nantakas! Surely, this was a sign that the weasel spirit would keep him safe all his life long.

Ever after, Nantakas kept weasel claws, a weasel tail, and bits of weasel fur in his bundle of good luck charms. He felt safe with the kingbird skin and the weasel claws hung round his neck when he went off to war.

Pocahontas did not smile while she watched the war party get into the great log canoe. How many of these brave young men would come safely back, she asked herself. Would Nantakas be left behind, wounded or dead? Would his scalp be carried off by the enemy tribe there in the west?

She felt better when the warriors brought the Okee from the temple in the forest. This image of the terrible Okeus had bones of wood, insides of moss, and skin of tanned deerskin. It went into every battle with the Powhatan braves. It gave them courage just to look at its ugly brown painted face, its white breast, and its spotted black and white body.

The copper chains and strings of white beads around the neck of the Okee shone bright in the sunlight. Surely, when the arrows began to fly, this powerful god would make the enemy run away.

When Pocahontas came back to the village, the boys were already playing the war game. Against their will, the smaller ones were pretending to be the enemy band. The bigger boys played the part of the brave Powhatans.

"I am Nantakas," cried a boy named Little Wolf. "Surely I will bring the most scalps from our dead enemies."

On the edge of the clearing beyond the wigwams, the boys had set up little shelters made of tree branches and grass. Willow wands were their war clubs. Blows from these might sting, but they would do no real harm.

The boys' pretend-arrows were thin spears of grass tied tightly together. And their tomahawks were of blunt wood which did not really cut. For a scalp, each boy had a tuft of grass stuck on the crown of his head.

If a grass arrow struck a part of a boy's body where a real arrow would kill, he had to fall down. His killer then put one foot on his shoulder and grabbed his grass scalp lock. With his wood knife, the lucky warrior pretended to cut it off. And, proudly, he hung

Nantakas Goes to War

the grass scalp from the deerskin belt around his bare body.

Like grown-up braves, these "Powhatans" hid behind trees on the edge of the clearing. The "enemy" hid, too, among their little grass wigwams.

Slowly, close to the ground, the "Powhatans" crept out of the bushes. Then with shrill war cries of *"Ow-ow-ow-ow,"* they attacked the grass village of the "enemy."

The boys' war game seemed almost real to Pocahontas and the other girls who were watching. The willow "war clubs" were dealing out stinging blows. Grass arrows were flying through the air.

Suddenly Little Wolf, the boy who was pretending he was Nantakas, ran out from behind a tree. By bad luck, he ran straight into the path of a flying arrow from the bow of Running Fox. And by worse luck, this was a real arrow instead of an arrow made out of grass.

The arrow's sharp stone point went deep into Little Wolf's leg. Try as he would, the boy could not pull it out. It hurt too much.

"It was my arrow. I know I should not have used a real arrow in the war game." Running Fox tried to excuse himself. "But, truly, I did not aim it at Little Wolf."

The other boys and girls went with Little Wolf to

ask his grandfather to get the arrow out of his leg. They watched while the man dug out its point with a sharp sliver of bone. Everyone praised Little Wolf because he did not cry out for the pain of his bleeding wound.

But Pocahontas was troubled. Was this not a bad sign? Did it not mean that her dear brother, the real Nantakas, would be wounded in the western fighting?

"Nantakas knows better than to run out into the path of a flying arrow," her mother tried to comfort the worried girl.

"I shall make offerings to Manito and to Okeus," Pocahontas declared. "I will give my fine necklace of shining white shells to the keeper of Okeus's temple. And you, my mother, will you give me a little tobacco and some red puccoon paint powder to throw into our fire? The smoke will carry these precious things out of the smoke hole and up to the good Manito in the sky."

The spirit offerings were made. Pocahontas raised her arms high, and she cried, "Manito, Great One, bend close to the earth! Look down on Nantakas! Keep him safe, out of the arrows' paths!"

"Okeus, wear my necklace of shining shells. And fight close by the side of Nantakas." So the girl sent out her earnest prayers to the spirits to protect her best-beloved brother.

The Mystery
of the White Manitos

Her fear for her brother made Pocahontas restless. She wandered from wigwam to wigwam. And at last she came to the porch of Thunder Eagle, the wise old medicine man.

"I bring you a gift of tobacco from The Powhatan's pouch, Grandfather," she said. "Tell me, Thunder Eagle, will Nantakas come safely home again from the western war?"

At first the old man did not look up from the magic rattle he was putting together. With smears of thick deer-horn glue, he made the wood handle fast in a hole in the yellow gourd. Pocahontas could hear the tiny stones, inside the gourd, rattle around as the old man worked.

"Nantakas will come home, Pocahontas," Thunder

Eagle said at last. "Nantakas is a Powhatan. And the Powhatans are the mightiest warriors in all this land. Only when the white tribe comes over the sea need we be afraid!"

Pocahontas was comforted by the words of the medicine man. If Nantakas came home, safe and sound, then all would be well for her.

But the girl was curious too, as she always was when anyone spoke of the white tribe which would one day come again across the Great Waters. Already the white tribe had been in the southland, in their giant canoes with wings like those of birds.

The Indians of the part of the country where their canoes had landed said the strangers had faces as pale as the moon. Some had blue eyes, and much hair on their chins. Many believed these pale men were white Manitos.

"Will the white Manitos ever come to Werowocomico, Thunder Eagle?" Pocahontas asked, sitting down on the porch platform beside the old man. For the moment she forgot her fears for her dear brother.

"Our grandfathers knew all things. They have said so, my child.

" 'Great shall the Powhatans be in this land,' they have said. 'But one day, out of the sunrise, across the great waters, there shall come a white tribe that shall be even greater.'

"Already the pale-faced men have come," Thunder Eagle went on. "They have come once and again, again and again. But each time they have gone away."

"Do you think the Pale Ones are from the spirit world, Thunder Eagle? Are they truly Manitos? Are they sent us by the Great Spirit?"

Thunder Eagle who talked with the spirits, could tell what was to happen.

"Who knows, little sister?" Thunder Eagle replied. "The Pale Faces come over the water, not out of Manito's home in the sky. But they ride the waves in canoes without any paddles. Gray wings like those of enormous birds fly over their boats. Surely their land must be a magic land where the trees are so huge that they can be hollowed out to make such giant canoes.

"I was a young man, Pocahontas, when I first heard of the white tribe. Travelers from lands to the south told me the story. Three giant canoes with wings brought the strangers there.

"The curious speech of the visitors frightened the people watching them from the shore. Some would have run away to hide in the forest. But the weroance said, 'Surely, these are spirit guests. One must not anger Manitos.' So they did not run away.

"Those tribes of the southland all made the white strangers welcome. Just as we do, they washed the feet of their guests. They spread mats for them to sit upon. They brought them deer meat, fresh fish, and sweet fruits.

"In return, the white visitors gave their hosts splendid gifts from their strange land across the wide waters. By smiles and by signs, the two peoples swore to love one another and to be friends and brothers.

"All through that summer, the strangers lived in peace there in the southland. When their winged canoes took them away in the Time of Falling Leaves, a young brave named Manteo went with them.

"With the next blooming of the dogwood," Thunder Eagle's story continued, "the white Manitos came back to that southland. This time there were seven canoes instead of three. And in these seven canoes there were many men with pale faces and hairy chins. Manteo was with them. He could now speak with the tongue of a white man. He could tell his own people just what the white Manitos said."

The next part of Thunder Eagle's tale was not so pleasant to hear.

"This time, the white Manitos forgot they had sworn to be brother-friends with the people of our country. Some of our people also forgot. In one town, a foolish boy stole a fine cup of precious white metal which shone like the moon.

"The strangers were angry. They did not wait for the weroance there to get their precious cup back for them. Instead, they burned down the wigwams of the young thief's town. They spoiled the good corn there, and there was none for the winter.

"After that, our people and their white visitors were always at war. Our people were brave. But they could not withstand the terrible thunder-tubes of the strangers." Thunder Eagle shuddered when he spoke of the guns of the white men.

"When the leaves began to fall, the Pale Faces went back to their own land. But they came again in the next Month of the Buds. This time, they built wigwams. And when the giant canoes went away, many Pale Faces stayed behind. They had brought their food with them from over the sea. They meant to stay through the winter here in our land."

"And did they stay, Thunder Eagle? Where are those men now?"

"No one tells what became of those white men, my child." The old man stopped speaking. He seemed to be looking far to the south. Perhaps he had once been there himself. Some even say it was the Powhatans who killed those white strangers.

"No one ever found out what became of those Pale Faces," the old man repeated. "When the giant canoes came again, they were gone. Their houses had been burned. They had left some strange marks upon a tree trunk. Their brothers thought these marks meant they had gone to a place called Croatan. But they were not at that place either."

"Did the white Manitos come again after that?" Pocahontas still was curious.

"They came once again, yes. And this time their wives and their children came with them. A baby girl was born there in the southland. But when the birds began to fly down from the north to their warm

The Mystery of the White Manitos

winter feeding grounds, the strangers all went away in their giant canoes."

Thunder Eagle and Pocahontas were silent. They were thinking and thinking of these curious people from across the Great Waters. Then the old man spoke again.

"Our grandfathers were wise. They have warned us that one day the white tribe will be greater in this land than our own people. The Pale Faces will come again. Of that we can be sure."

The old medicine man's talk about the white Manitos had made Pocahontas forget her brother's danger. When she ran back to her father's wigwam, she was thinking only of the white strangers. She was trying hard to imagine what these strange men would be like.

Surely, if they were Manitos, they would bring good luck to her land. The Great Spirit Himself must have taught these Pale Faces to make their magic thunder-tubes which could kill from so far away. Surely, then, they were Manitos.

It would be exciting to have them come again. That is, of course, if they came as the brother-friends of the Indians, not as their foes.

The Victory Dance

"I HEAR them! I hear them singing!" Pocahontas cried as she swam quickly to the river bank.

Before any of the other girls or boys, she was out of the water. Like a squirrel, she was high up in a tree, looking to see whether the songs were from the war canoe, coming home.

"They are at the bend of the river. *Hi-yay! Hi-yay!* Go tell it in the wigwams! Our men return, singing the victory song."

The children ran fast to spread the good news. Out of the wigwams, men and women came running. By the time the great log canoe reached the landing place, all the people of Werowocomico were there. Again and again, they were tapping their open mouths to make their glad cry, *"Ow-ow-ow-ow! Ow-ow-ow-ow!"*

The Victory Dance

The song of the returning braves rang over the water:

> *"The bird of war flew before us!*
> *Eagle feathers shall we wear!"*

An eagle feather for every enemy killed was the rule in their land.

> *"Eagle feathers, many eagle feathers*
> *You shall wear!"*

The people on the river bank sang the victory song with them. It was a fine sight, that procession of the warriors to the open gathering place in the center of Werowocomico. First marched the brave men who had brought home scalps of the enemy.

"Nantakas! Nantakas!" Pocahontas saw her brother near the head of the line. Swiftly she ran to him. And she threw her arms about him.

"Little sister! Little sister! You may be my scalp-bearer!" The young man handed Pocahontas two thin, long poles. From their ends dangled the scalps he had taken from the enemies he had killed.

Pocahontas was proud to be carrying in her own hands the proofs of her brother's boldness in battle. Scalping was the custom with all her people. It did not seem cruel to this Indian girl. Usually the small patch of skin with its long lock of black hair was not cut off until its owner had been killed.

"Without scalps, how could a warrior prove he had truly killed the enemies he claimed?" So her father, The Powhatan, spoke of this custom to his children.

Far and wide, in America then, the men always left one long lock of hair upon their shaved crowns. Not to do so, they thought, was to be unfair to those against whom they fought.

Many scalps were waving in the summer breeze on that day in Werowocomico. All had been washed clean in a river. Fastened on little hoops made of bent twigs, the skins had dried hard. These scalps would be shown for many years to prove how brave their takers had been.

The children, running beside the returned warriors, were specially interested in one prisoner who had been brought back in the war canoe. This prisoner was young. He was very young. Surely he could not have seen more than fifteen autumn flights of the birds.

"How proudly that strange boy holds his head!" Pocahontas said to Little Wolf. Later she learned that he was White Owl, the son of the weroance of the enemy tribe.

The women looked all along the line of the marchers. Each one wanted to make sure her own men had come home. One woman ran to her wounded husband, who was being carried on a bed made of tree poles.

Another woman, a mother called Yellow Bird, searched in vain for her son.

The Victory Dance

"Your son has gone to Manito's Sky Land," Nantakas told Yellow Bird gently. "He died fighting bravely. We had to leave him behind."

Tears rolled down the woman's cheeks. But she did not cry out. Sadly, and in silence, she made her way alone into her wigwam.

There was joy and excitement that afternoon in the town of Werowocomico. Men, women, and children gathered in the open space in the midst of the wigwams. There they listened to the young braves make their "kill talks," and tell just how it was in that western war.

"All through the night we fought under the full moon," they said, "and by morning, many of the enemy were dead. The others had run away."

Everyone listening then gave the shrill wavering victory call. *"Ow-ow-ow-ow! Ow-ow-ow-ow!"*

The children shouted for joy *"Hi-yay! Hi-yay!"*

Food for a feast was heaped on the wood platters in the village gathering place. Facing the painted post in its center, a pile of deerskins was laid down for The Powhatan to sit upon. Pocahontas ran to squat by his side to watch the victory dance.

"Our people are proud of us!
Our people tell of our eagle feathers!"

This was one of the songs sung by the young men as they "danced their scalps."

They waved their little wood poles with the scalps floating upon them like tiny flags. They stamped their feet, and they jumped about in their wild dance. Their dark eyes were bright. Their white teeth flashed as they yelled their war cries once again.

The women and children clapped their hands in time to the beat of the drums. Whistles called with shrill voices. Pocahontas shook her gourd rattle as hard as any of the medicine men. The hickory nuts inside it made a fine noise.

When the dancers were tired, they thrust the ends of their scalp poles into the ground. People then brought them gifts. Arrows and shell tools! Deerskins and strings of beads! These and other treasures were their rewards for the brave deeds they had performed.

"Where is the young prisoner?" The Powhatan asked. "Let him now come before me!"

Pocahontas did not like this part of a victory celebration. So often, as today, the prisoners looked like fine, brave young men. It was sad that they had to be treated as enemies. But, of course, they were enemies, and it was the custom.

The eyes of White Owl, the young son of the enemy weroance, were steady. He walked proudly. Not

The braves made their "kill talks" and proudly displayed the scalps they had taken from their enemies.

The Victory Dance

once did he try to break away from the men who led him before the Powhatan king.

"This one must be brave to have been in the battle. He is hardly more than a boy," the people said to each other.

"Our prisoner is the son of the weroance whose tribe killed our brothers, Red Cloud and Great Turtle." The Powhatan's voice was cold and hard. "We Powhatans punish when our brothers are killed. Let this prisoner die! Let the firewood be brought!"

"O, no, my father," Pocahontas cried out. "Let it not be the fire for this brave young boy!"

"Let the firewood be brought!" The Powhatan turned his face away from the pleading eyes of his daughter. "And let the news of his son's dying be sent to his father!"

The men piled the sticks of wood about the feet of the young prisoner. In those times in this wild land, death by the war club, or death by the fire, was often the fate of enemies taken in battle.

White Owl did not speak. In his own tribe, he knew, it would have been just like this if Nantakas, the son of The Powhatan, had been his father's prisoner.

No sign of fear showed on the face of the boy. He was determined to die as a great chief's son should. He raised his arms high and he sang in a loud voice:

"*Great Father in the Sky,
Look down on White Owl.*

"*Great Father in the Sky,
Help White Owl to die bravely.*"

A blazing torch was brought out from a nearby wigwam fire. Its flaming end was about to touch the dry bits of wood at the prisoner's feet.

Then, out of the crowd, the woman, Yellow Bird, ran to kneel before Powhatan.

"My son is dead. My wigwam is empty. I have no one to bring me deer from the forest or fish from the river. I ask for this young man in the place of my dead son."

"*Ah-h-h-h-h-h!*" a great sigh came from the crowd of watching women. This brave lad was worthy to be one of their tribe. They would be glad if his life could be spared.

"The battle took a son away from you, Yellow Bird. The battle shall give a son back to you. It is the custom!" So The Powhatan gave his consent. Perhaps his old heart, too, had been touched by the bravery of the boy.

The torch was thrown down to burn away on the bare ground. And White Owl stepped forth from amid the awesome pile of firewood.

Pocahontas was happy as she watched Yellow Bird

The Victory Dance

lead her new son away to her wigwam. She knew that White Owl's welcome into her tribe would not take place until after the victory had been danced for many nights. But the boy now was as safe as her own brothers.

At last the scalps were put away. The singing and the dancing were over. And White Owl's bed mat was spread each night in the wigwam of his new mother, Yellow Bird.

A Fight with a Fish

THE morning sky was still rosy red with the sunrise. But Pocahontas and Little Wolf and other boys and girls of the village were already on the river banks.

"This is the day for Gray Hawk to take his new canoe out on the river," Pocahontas had told her mother as she jumped out of bed. "Nantakas and Gray Hawk are going after the big fish in the new canoe."

For many moons Pocahontas had watched the young Indian, Gray Hawk, at work on his log boat. It took a long time to cut a fine canoe like this one out of a tree.

First Gray Hawk had made a broad band of fire around the tree trunk. Sometimes the children had helped him pat wet mud on each side of the smoking

A Fight with a Fish

bark. This kept the fire from spreading where it was not wanted.

When the burned part of the tree trunk was black and soft, Gray Hawk cut it away with his sharp stone tools. Then he set the tree afire again.

By burning and cutting, Gray Hawk felled the tree. By burning, and cutting, and scraping away the burned parts, he made his canoe.

The canoe Gray Hawk was making was not a very big boat. It would only hold about ten or twelve men. It took many, many Indians, working a long time, to make a great war canoe which would carry thirty or forty.

Burning and scraping! Burning and scraping! Day after day Gray Hawk had patiently worked at his task. Now his new canoe was ready.

Until it touches the water, a boat builder cannot be sure how good a boat he has built. Pocahontas and the other girls and boys had watched Gray Hawk's log canoe slide into the river on the day before. They held their breath. And then they all cheered. Like a wild duck, the canoe rode squarely and surely upon the water.

Like an arrow, the new canoe sped over the river. The children cried out, "Good! Good!" For Gray Hawk had a new canoe as fast as any boat on the Pamunkey that day. It would be strong enough, easily, to bring home the big fish.

In the light of the dawn, now, Nantakas and several other friends of Gray Hawk were already seated in the new log canoe.

On the boat's bottom were nets to take fish out of the river. There were dipping nets to scoop the fish out of the fish traps when the tide was low. There were spears to stab the fish that would swim close to the canoe. And there were bows and arrows to shoot those fish that were farther away.

"I wish I could come with you and Nantakas, Gray Hawk!" Pocahontas spoke longingly. She had been helping the men carry their lines and their nets down to the river.

"Fishing for the big fish is not for women or girls," Gray Hawk spoke kindly. "And today, little sister, we hope to bring back a sturgeon."

"I will get you some more mussel pearls for your necklace, Little Snow Feather," Nantakas called out, as the paddles pushed the log boat away from the river bank.

Pocahontas held her hand high to wish them good luck. She did not take her eyes from the river until their boat had gone out of sight.

On the porch beside her wigwam, Pocahontas found her mother at work, making a new arrow quiver for The Powhatan. The woman was weaving the little case out of reeds and silk grass. The straight

A Fight with a Fish

slender reeds were laid down side by side. Then strong cords of twisted silk grass were woven over and under them.

"It is good that the men go to catch the big fish." Her mother nodded her head when Pocahontas told her of Gray Hawk's words. "The cold, hungry winter moons are not far away. The great sturgeon is good for smoking and keeping. Sturgeon is good to have when there is ice on the river."

Pocahontas herself often fished with the other children. In the small streams of her land, the Indian boys and girls made little fish traps like those which the men set at the mouths of the rivers. With sticks, cleverly woven together with thin strips of green oak wood, they fenced in little yards, down under the water.

High tide brought the waters of Chesapeake Bay into the rivers of Powhatan's land. The rivers rose up and up between their banks. Then the fish could swim easily into the traps.

At low tide, the rivers fell until the tops of the fish traps were above water. The fish could not swim out again then over the trap fences. It was easy to scoop them out with hand nets. Sometimes, in the streams of this Powhatan country, the fish were so many that the boys and girls could catch them with their own hands.

When Gray Hawk's canoe came back up the river, the women and girls had already set out the wood drying racks. All ran down to the river to help unload the fish. In baskets on their backs they brought in the bass and the salmon, the perch and the other smaller fish.

"Hey! Hey! O-hey!" Everyone was astonished at the giant sturgeon which the men untied from the end of Gray Hawk's canoe. That fish was as long as Nantakas was tall. It was twice as heavy as Gray Hawk.

There had not been room for the sturgeon in the log canoe. So the fishermen had pulled it along through the water behind the boat. Pocahontas could see the heavy rope of braided deerskin tied round its tail.

"It was Nantakas who brought this Grandfather Fish to our boat," Gray Hawk told the women. "And it was a mighty battle he had with this great one when he threw his rope noose round his tail."

Pocahontas listened with shining eyes to the exciting story of her big brother's brave fight with the giant sturgeon.

"Grandfather Sturgeon swam beside us," Nantakas said. "Perhaps he thought our canoe was some strange kind of fish. For he played with it in the water. Once he even made a great leap, clear over our boat. He came so close that it was not hard to get my rope noose around his huge tail.

"As soon as the fish felt the bite of the rope, he swam away. Grandfather Sturgeon was strong. He pulled

A Fight with a Fish

me out of the canoe into the river. But I did not let go my end of the rope.

"I swam back toward the boat. The sturgeon pulled me away. There, in the water, we fought, the fish and I.

"Then Gray Hawk brought his boat very near. The fish was growing tired. Gray Hawk gave him a blow on his nose with a club, which helped a great deal. Soon our battle was over."

"In all his excitement in fighting with the fish, Nantakas surely forgot to get mussel pearls for my necklace," Pocahontas was thinking when the story was finished. But, of course, she said nothing.

However, as soon as Nantakas stepped out upon the river bank, he threw her a little wet deerskin bag. It had been hung round his neck on a thin cord of deer sinew.

"I did not forget, little sister," he said. It was as if he already knew what she had been thinking. "Inside this bag there are five pearls for your necklace. I dived down to the river bottom to get the mussels. And I had time to open them before Grandfather Sturgeon here came along."

In her tawny hand, the five mussel pearls looked as white as the clouds up in the sky. Perhaps these pearls were not quite so bright as the pearls that sometimes are made inside an oyster. But oyster pearls were rare in the waters of Powhatan's country. Pearls from mussels were almost as pretty.

The giant sturgeon was soon cleaned and cut up into pieces. Pocahontas and the other girls laid the long thin strips of fish over the drying racks. Above the slow smoky fire of hickory wood, the fish would dry hard. Hickory smoke would give it a fine taste when it was boiled soft again for winter stews.

Brave Otter Makes Rain

THE sun shone bright and hot in the summer sky. Not a cloud was to be seen. It was many days since rain had fallen on the corn fields around Werowocomico.

"O, Sun!" Pocahontas said as she looked up at the blue heavens, "O, great Grandfather Sun, hide your face behind clouds! Let rain come to our thirsty corn fields today!"

Each day the women looked more sadly at their drooping corn-stalks. They thought how they had worked to make the corn grow, ever since the Month of the Buds. And they shook their heads.

"If Manito does not soon send us rain, our corn will burn up. We shall have no food for the winter. We shall have to use the bark off the trees for making our bread."

Powhatan himself sent up prayers to the Great Spirit.

"Father," he prayed, "Thou who canst make the sun and rain do thy bidding, look on our dry land! Cover this burning sun with thy rain clouds! Send the war whoops of thy thunder to shake the water out of the clouds!"

But no rain came. No thunder was heard, not even far, far away.

"Thunder Eagle, make thy magic," the women cried at the door of the old medicine man's wigwam. "Make charms for Okeus! Surely, it is because of his anger that our corn plants bend their heads toward the ground."

Thunder Eagle brought together the best of his charms. He put on his headdress of stuffed snakeskins and weasel tails. He put on his necklaces and bracelets of sharp, curving bears' claws. With his face painted more fiercely than ever before, he was fearful to see. Pocahontas was sure he could frighten even Okeus who was keeping the rain clouds out of her sky.

Thunder Eagle danced the Rain Dance. He sang songs to the Rain Spirit. But no rain came. The proud heads of the cornstalks drooped lower and lower.

Other medicine men tried their prayers and their magic. But each day it was the same. The sun shone, burning hot, in a cloudless sky.

The medicine men were ashamed that their magic

did not make rain. But they did not show how they felt.

"It is that the Great Spirit has already heard our prayers for rain too often. It is new magic he wants. It must be one of our young men whose prayers he will answer."

At first the young men of Werowocomico would not try to make rain. They were afraid that they, too, would fail.

Still, it would be a fine thing if one of them should succeed. A man who made rain now, would have strong medicine. And a new medicine man would be honored all through the land.

Three young men at last decided to try to bring rain down from the sky to save the wilting corn. The first, Whirling Bear, was more bold than he was wise. He covered his face all over with white paint. Then, with his fingers, he drew circles of red paint around his eyes. He made streaks of black across his white cheeks. He added blue paint as well.

"I shall look so fierce that the spirits which hold back the rain clouds will be frightened away," he told his friends.

Whirling Bear climbed up on top of a wigwam whose arched roof rose high under the blue sky. The people gathered to watch him as he raised his arms and commanded the clouds to appear.

They stood there a long time. But the clouds did not come at Whirling Bear's call. The sun shone as bright and hot as before.

Whirling Bear had to climb down again. His magic had failed. "It was not the day to make rain," he said, trying to excuse himself.

Turkey Tail and Brave Otter were the names of the two other young braves who said they would try to make the rain come.

"Brave Otter can do it, if anyone can," Pocahontas said the next day. She thought this young man was by far the wisest of the three. Brave Otter was a good hunter. Brave Otter's boat always was full of fish when he came back up the river.

Brave Otter took a long look at the sky. He shaded his eyes with his tawny hand. He looked to the north, to the south, to the east. Longest of all, he looked to the west whence the summer rain clouds most often came. Not a wisp of cloud did he see there. And he shook his head.

"Perhaps tomorrow I will try," he said. "Not today."

"Brave Otter, make rain for us!" Pocahontas said the next day.

The young man shook his head. Still there was no sign of clouds in the west.

"The time for my magic has not yet come," he said.

Brave Otter Makes Rain

"Let Turkey Tail try today, if he likes. I will wait yet a little."

The Powhatans smiled. They were fond of the young man called Turkey Tail. He was a good youth. But, all knew, there was not a more stupid fellow in all Werowocomico.

"Look at poor Turkey Tail!" the people said as the clumsy youth scrambled up on top of the wigwam roof. He dropped his gourd rattle twice, and at last he had to carry it up in his mouth.

"The others only said prayers," Turkey Tail shouted down. "But prayers are not enough. I shall dance the Rain Dance up here where Manito can see me. Surely that will please him so much that he will send rain."

Now, the roof of this wigwam, like the others of this village, was arched like a rainbow across the sky. Its cover of mats was laid upon curving young tree trunks. How could anyone dance on such a curving roof?

But, when his prayers had been said, Turkey Tail began to stamp and to caper. He sang while he jumped up and down. And in time to his song, he shook the gourd rattle which he had held between his teeth when he climbed up on the roof.

Perhaps this young man was right. Everyone knew that dances pleased Manito. But a wigwam roof was no place for a dance. The people shook their heads. And they smiled while they waited to see what would happen.

Suddenly a great laugh rose from the crowd. Turkey Tail had leaped up into the air. And when he came down again, he went right through the roof mats of that wigwam. It was lucky his deerskin belt caught on the end of a pole under the roof. Or he might have broken his neck.

As it was, Turkey Tail hung there, just over the fire hole. The other young men had to climb up and set him free.

How the people laughed then! For days the children teased Turkey Tail, asking him to dance his Rain Dance once more up on the roof.

Now there was only Brave Otter left to try to make rain. The next morning, the young man came out very early to look at the sky. The sun still shone bright and hot. But, far off in the west, the sky seemed to be dark. Surely, surely, there were clouds moving slowly up out of the west. Brave Otter threw a small feather into the air. He nodded his head when he saw that wind from the west blew it toward the sunrise.

"I will try my magic today," Brave Otter said then.

"Brave Otter will make rain today!" Pocahontas spread the news.

The people waited while the young man put on his

Brave Otter Makes Rain

body paint. Pocahontas helped him dust his freshly painted skin with soft, downy birds' feathers of many colors. The feathers clung to the moist paint. Everyone thought they made Brave Otter look very fine. The people were so busy watching the young rainmaker get ready that they did not notice the very dark clouds that were now in the west.

On top of the wigwam roof, Brave Otter prayed to Manito.

"Great Spirit," he called. "Ruler of our sky, look down on our thirsty plants! Send us rain water to save our corn!"

"Wingan! Wingan! (Good! Good!)" the people below murmured. And then someone cried out, "See! A cloud comes! A cloud comes to Werowocomico. Manito already has heard Brave Otter's prayer."

"Spirit-that-rides-the-West-Wind, blow this rain cloud to Werowocomico!" Brave Otter shouted another prayer up into the sky.

Pocahontas ran into Powhatan's wigwam. She threw a pinch of her father's finest tobacco onto the fire.

"This is for thee, Great Okeus," she cried. She wanted to take that Wicked One's thoughts away from the blessed rain cloud. In this way she hoped he would not blow the cloud away from over her village before the rain could fall from it.

When Pocahontas ran out of the wigwam again, the

dark cloud was hanging just above the young rain-maker. Against its blackness, she could see Brave Otter, with his bow drawn and his arrow pointing upward.

"Come down, O Rain!" Brave Otter commanded. "Fall on our corn fields!" And he shot first one arrow, then another arrow, up towards the black cloud that had come out of the west.

"Listen! Manito speaks to Brave Otter!" Powhatan cried. The old weroance was standing in the crowd beside the wigwam. He had heard the low rumble of thunder come out of the cloud.

"Manito answers Brave Otter!" the shout rose from the crowd. Another thunderclap! And then blessed raindrops began to fall on their upturned eager faces.

Brave Otter did not need to send up any more arrows. The rain fell in torrents. Like the great waterfalls far up the Powhatan River, it poured out of the sky.

Shouting for joy, the people took shelter inside their wigwams. It rained and it rained. When the thunder was no longer heard, the rain still kept falling upon the thirsty ground.

For one day, for two days, for three days it rained. The cornstalks waved their leaves high in the air once again. By the end of the three days, the plants stood up straight and strong.

Brave Otter shot first one arrow, then another up towards the black cloud.

Brave Otter Makes Rain

The corn was saved. Brave Otter had brought the rain just in time.

Many gifts were laid down in the wigwam of the young rainmaker. Wampum belts, deer hides, moccasins and fishhooks, arrows and clamshell knives were brought to him by the grateful people of Werowocomico.

No one even hinted that the rain might have come even if Brave Otter had not called upon Manito and shot arrows into the cloud. They only said, "Brave Otter has strong magic. Brave Otter makes powerful medicine for our Powhatan tribe."

The Feast of the Green Corn

"Hear us talking, Great Spirit!
Hear us thanking Thee for the corn!

"Thou art our Great Father!
The Earth is our Great Mother!

"Hear us thanking Thee for the corn!"

Powhatan stood with both arms raised to the sky. About him, crowded into the open gathering space, were men, women and children. All listened in silence to the words he was sending up to Manito.

It was the Great Feast of the Green Corn. Indians from towns up and down the river had come in their

The Feast of the Green Corn

canoes to Werowocomico to join in this thanksgiving celebration.

"Is the corn ripe enough, Grandmother?"

For many mornings this had been the question which Thunder Eagle asked old Moon-in-the-Dawn. Moon-in-the-Dawn was the oldest of all the women in Werowocomico. She had been tending corn longer than any other. So it was surely she who would know best when the fat ears on the tall stalks were ready for eating.

At last, Thunder Eagle had come to The Powhatan. "Moon-in-the-Dawn says the green corn is ready, Wahunsonacock," the medicine man reported.

"Wingan! Wingan! It is good. Let the runners be called," Powhatan ordered. And when the young men stood before him, he said, "Tell it along the river. The green corn is ready. The feast will begin when the sun has risen again, and once again."

Now it was The Day. Near the fire in the center of the village meeting place were great baskets of corn—white, yellow, and red. Blue and many other colors were mixed in the grains on some ears.

Thunder Eagle was looking more fearsome than ever. He was wearing a new headdress with a stuffed hawk on the top. His face and his body were painted with streaks and circles of red, black, and white.

The young warriors who were to take part in the

Dance of the Green Corn were finely painted as well. Everyone, that day, was wearing some paint on his skin. Even Pocahontas had spots of red puccoon paint on her cheeks, and red stripes on her shoulders.

Some of the young men had a dusting of bright-colored birds' feathers on their well-greased bodies. Their heads were newly shaved on the right side. This was the Powhatan custom. Long hair on the right side would be in the way of their bows when they were hunting or fishing.

Long black locks of hair were allowed to grow on the left sides of their heads. These were wound into sleek knots that shone like a crow's wing. One young man had for a hairpin a quill tipped with a rattle from a grandfather rattlesnake.

Brave Otter wore a small wriggling green snake tied to his ear. And many of the other young braves had the wings and heads of bright birds on their headbands. O, those young Powhatans made a fine sight that day, when they gathered for the Dance of the Green Corn.

"I shall wear my necklace of copper links and mussel pearls," Pocahontas said. And she put it over her head with her other strings of shining white and colored shell beads. Like all the other girls and the boys, she was smiling. This was the happiest day of her year.

For the first time, that day, Pocahontas was wearing the small deerskin skirt of a grown-up girl. She was nearly twelve years old now.

Her mother had made her this little skirt of softest deerskin. There were fringes cut into its edges. And there was a pattern of beads and colored porcupine quills sewed on its front.

Pocahontas was proud of her grown-up clothes. Until now, in warm weather, like all other Indian children, she had wanted only to be free. Clothes were a bother when one ran through the woods, or when one wanted to swim.

Powhatan had taken his seat on the mat of honor. The drums were ready. Thunder Eagle, the chief medicine man, stepped into the center of the dancers. In one hand he held up his magic gourd rattle. In the other was a tall cornstalk with its long grasslike leaves.

In the circle around Thunder Eagle, the other medicine men and the young warriors stood waiting. Each one held proudly his tall stalk of corn. The crowd of watchers pressed close.

The fire was already laid. The stone pot that stood over it was already filled with water.

Then White Crow and Little Hawk, the best firemakers of the village, squatted down beside a pile of dry sticks and leaves.

Silently, the crowd watched while White Crow rolled the fire stick around and around between the palms of his hands. Its point was whirling inside a hole in a block of hard wood which Little Hawk held firmly down on the ground.

Around and around went the fire stick. When White Crow called *"Hey!"*—like magic, the whirling stick passed from his hands to the hands of Little Hawk. So quickly did the stick change hands that its whirling never slowed down.

"Fire! There is fire!" The shout rose from the crowd of watchers when the first bright spark was blown out upon the dry leaves. The first flame was followed by all the leaves catching fire, then the sticks of dry wood.

This was the signal for the dancing to begin. The drums beat. The people began to chant the Song of the Green Corn. Lifting their feet, slowly at first, then faster and faster, the dancers moved round the pot.

Their dancing was faster still when the ears of corn for Manito were thrown into the boiling water. Their rattles shook. Their cornstalks waved. Pocahontas always said this Corn Dance was the best of all her people's dances.

Now Manito's corn was ready for eating. Pocahontas licked her lips as the steaming ears were taken out of the water. It was too bad that this corn could not be put into someone's mouth, she thought. But, of course, it was important that Manito should have the first taste.

The Feast of the Green Corn

The cooked corn was dropped into the fire. There, it quickly burned to ashes. When its smoke rose into the air, Pocahontas was sure it would go all the way up to Manito in his Sky Land. It would take with it the grateful thanks of the Powhatans for their good corn harvest.

"Now they will build the new fire! They will cook the corn for us to eat," Pocahontas said to Little Wolf who was standing beside her.

The new fire was quickly laid. The firemakers, White Crow and Little Hawk, fanned the embers of the old fire into flames that set fire to the new wood under the pot. Soon the water boiled once again, and more corn was cooked.

For seven days, the Powhatans feasted upon their green corn. They ate deer and squirrels, oysters and fish. For seven days, they sang and they danced the Corn Dance.

At last, the time came when no one could eat any more corn. The deer meat and the fish, that had been baked for the feast, now were all gone. The canoes of the visitors had been paddled away. Werowocomico was quiet once more.

In this year of 1607, the corn crop was good. Two, three, even four fat ears hung on the tall stalks in the corn patches. In spite of all that had been eaten at the Feast of the Green Corn, there would be many full baskets to store in the ground pits and the wooden corncribs.

"I am thinking of a story about corn, my father," Pocahontas said to The Powhatan. It was just after the Corn Feast and she was sitting beside him on his wigwam porch.

"Tell the story to me, Little Snow Feather." Powhatan looked fondly down at the girl by his knees. Children often repeated the old tales they had heard from their fathers and mothers. It was by telling them over and over that the Indians made sure their old tales should not be forgotten.

"I am thinking of the story of how the good corn was once almost lost to man," Pocahontas began. "You yourself told me how it was, Wahunsonacock.

"It was long, long ago, when the world was still very young. The Great Spirit was angry. For a certain man and woman he had made did not care for their corn fields. They let the weeds choke their corn plants. They let the animals that walk on four legs pull down the stalks. It was not strange that they had so little corn for planting their fields the next spring.

"When the buds came out on the trees once again, the man and the woman carried their baskets of seed corn out to their corn field.

"But, to their surprise, when they opened the baskets, each tiny grain of corn sprouted two little wings.

The Feast of the Green Corn

Like a swarm of mosquitoes, the corn grains flew up into the air and out of their sight.

" 'Our seed corn! It is gone! We have none now to plant!' the woman cried out.

" 'There are still a few more grains in the bag which we kept in our wigwam,' the man tried to comfort his wife.

"But when he opened that bag, he found it was filled with huge flying ants. Each ant flew away with a grain of corn held between its front legs. And there was none left.

" 'What shall we do now?' the woman asked her husband. 'How shall we plant our corn field? And if we do not have corn, what shall we use for cakes and for soup in winter's Hungry Time?'

" 'We must pray to Manito for help,' the man then decided.

"So they climbed to a high place under the sky. They made a fire there, on a great rock. Its smoke floated upward, towards the Great Spirit.

" 'Manito, Great One,' they prayed, lifting their arms towards the sky. 'Forgive us that we did not take better care of our corn. Send us more for the new planting. And never, never again will we forget what you taught us.'

"The man and the woman went back to their corn field. To their surprise, they found there was still a handful of corn in one of the baskets. Perhaps it had been there all the time, and they had overlooked it. Or, perhaps, it had been put there by Manito in answer to their prayers.

"That man was so happy that he danced round the basket. He sang songs of thanks to Manito. And when the woman looked into the basket again, she saw it held three times as much corn as there had been in it before.

"Each time the man danced, there was more corn for his new planting. And that, Wahunsonacock," Pocahontas ended the tale, "that is how people first knew that a Corn Dance would be pleasing to the Great Spirit."

The Great Deer Hunt

THE procession of log canoes was moving up the broad Pamunkey River. Blue-white autumn mist hung over the trees along the river banks. Like tobacco smoke, it softened the flaming reds of the maple trees. Like a thin curtain, it partly hid the yellow and russet hues of the poplars, the walnut trees, and the oaks.

"Manito is smoking his great pipe today," Pocahontas said to her mother as she watched the drifting mist.

"May his giant pipe keep the Great Spirit happy! May he smile down upon us and show us the place where many deer are." The Indian woman spoke as if she truly believed the mist came from the pipe of Manito.

Many log canoes were on the river this day. In the

morning stillness, one could hear the music of their paddles dipping in and out of the water. In the canoes there were families not only from Werowocomico but from many other villages along the Pamunkey.

It was the time of the Great Deer Hunt. Already the leaves were beginning to fall. Already the wild geese were flying south. *"Co-honk! Co-honk!"* Their cries could be heard often, telling, "Winter is near."

Deerskins must be had for making warm clothing and strong moccasins. Deer meat must be dried and smoked for the coming Hungry Time.

"Gather your spears and your arrows together!" The Powhatan sent out this word to all the men along the river.

"Roll up the mats for the hunting shelters!" This was his message to the women.

In all the small river towns, there was bustle and excitement. Men, women, and children were soon ready for another adventure into the wild western hills. There would be much work for the women there. The children could not well be left behind. And they, too, would help.

The boatmen sang as they paddled. Others joined in their songs. The autumn air was fresh. The sun soon burned the morning mist away and the sky was blue overhead.

Along both sides of the river, tall trees stretched their branches up, up, and up. It was as if they, too,

The Great Deer Hunt

were reaching to the Great Spirit for strength. Here and there, Pocahontas saw a deer on the river bank. Fish swam so close to her canoe that she could touch them with her fingers.

While her boat slid over the water, Pocahontas thought of all these good gifts from Manito. Great rivers to travel on! Tall trees for building wigwams! Forests full of fat deer and wild turkeys! Storehouses in the villages filled with corn, beans, and pumpkins! Truly, her father was right when he said the Great Spirit had given the Powhatans a wonderful land.

At night camps were made on the banks of the river. But, with the first rosy glow in the morning sky, the canoes moved on again. Up, always up the river they went. There were not enough deer near the villages where most of these people lived. For their autumn deer hunt, the Powhatans usually traveled for many sleeps to the wilder western parts of their land between the Pamunkey and the Chickahominy rivers.

"Will my father stay this year in his wigwam here in Orapax?" Pocahontas asked her mother when, at last, they came to this town.

"No, Little Snow Feather, The Powhatan says he will sleep with the hunters out in the forest. He will lead the deer hunt himself."

The Great Deer Hunt was the most exciting journey of the year for Pocahontas and her people. More than two hundred Powhatans were gathered here in this strange wilderness, beyond the town of Orapax.

Everyone was busy. The men were cutting down tall young trees to make the light frames of their hunting shelters. The women were laying the reed mats, which they had brought with them, over these frames. Soon, in the wilderness, there was a small village of rough little wigwams, set up in a great circle.

Scouts who had run off into the deep woods were soon back again. And they brought welcome news.

"We have found the deer, Wahunsonacock!" they cried to Powhatan. "The deer are many this year. And they are not far away."

No matter how many deer were taken in the Great Hunt each year, there always were more when the *co-honks* of the wild geese going south sounded again.

The scouts had found their deer on a long point of land. It would be easy to build a line of fires across the neck of this point. To get away from the fire, the deer would run towards the water. They could easily be taken by the hunters who would be hiding along the river bank there.

"It is the time to draw the lots," The Powhatan said to the hunters when the shelters were built, and the evening sun was low in the sky. In this way each year, it was decided which men should set the fires, and which ones should hide to kill the deer at the water's edge.

The Great Deer Hunt

Before the sun rose next morning, the camp was astir. Pocahontas and the other girls and the boys were already out to watch the hunters set forth. Silently, silently, lest they be noticed and sent back, the children followed the men.

When the hunters came to the place where they would set the woods on fire, the boys and girls climbed into tall trees. Up there, at a safe distance, they could see what went on.

Powhatan threw a small bird's feather up into the air. Carefully, he watched to see which way it would drift on the morning breeze.

"It is good!" he said to the waiting men. "The wind blows towards the river. It will carry our fire where we want it to go."

The old Chief raised his two arms to the sky.

"Great Spirit," he prayed. "Look down upon us! Walk by our side! Give us many deer for our winter cooking pots!"

Next the Chief sent up another prayer.

"O, Spirit of Fire! Send your red arrows now into this forest! Help us to drive the deer towards the water!"

Then Powhatan gave the signal to light the fires. Flaming torches were set to little piles of dry grass, leaves, and twigs. All across the great point of land where the deer were, fires were started. Soon red flames were licking the trunks of the trees. The wind blew the fire on and on through the woods.

Smoke filled the air. The flames crackled and roared. Pocahontas and her friends, up in the trees, could see rabbits and squirrels running for their lives, out from between the patches of fire.

With shrill cries, birds flew up into the air. Wild turkeys passed, half running, half flying, just under the trees where the children were. There was the sound of many deer, crashing through the bushes in their flight before the flames.

"*Hoka! Hey! Hoka! Hey!*" the hunters were shouting fiercely behind the fleeing deer.

Other hunters, with arrows and spears ready, waited in their hiding places in the bushes at the riv-

The Great Deer Hunt

er's edge. Soon they were killing the panting deer that came rushing for safety into the stream.

By the time of High Sun, fifteen fat deer had already been taken. Beside the hunting shelters, Pocahontas and the other children had gathered piles of clean leaves. On these the fresh deer meat would be laid down. The children helped the women, also, to set up the drying frames over the smoky fires they had made on the ground.

The women laughed and talked while they cut up the deer meat. Each one tried to cut her strips of meat longer and thinner than those of her neighbor. They worked fast with their cutting tools, which were made of sharp clamshells or the hard stone called flint.

All through this hunting camp the fresh raw meat made spots of red even brighter than the maple leaves overhead. The meat that was drying over the smoky fires was soon as brown as the dark oak leaves.

Day after day, the Great Deer Hunt went on. First the forest was fired in one place, then in another. And, often, a hunter went far-off from the others to seek deer by himself.

"Nantakas has turned himself into a deer. Come and see!" Pocahontas called to her friends one morning, midway through the hunt.

The young man had hidden himself inside a deer's

skin. It covered his shoulders and hung down his back. With one hand inside the head, Nantakas held the horns high. When her brother walked off into the woods, Pocahontas could see only the deer horns moving through the leaves of the trees.

Day after day the Great Deer Hunt went on.

The Great Deer Hunt

Nantakas walked softly. His keen eyes soon picked up the trail of a deer. By its tracks in the soft earth, he could tell just where it had gone. And soon he saw, through the trees, a fine fat young buck, drinking from a stream.

Twice that young buck raised his head from the water. He looked all around him. Like Pocahontas, no doubt, the animal saw only the head and the horns of another deer. He did not seem afraid.

The buck stood very still. And the flying arrow from the bow of the young hunter sped to its mark. Another deer was thus added to that day's take in the Great Deer Hunt.

That very same day Little Wolf said to Pocahontas, "This morning I shall hunt turkeys. I brought my own bow in our canoe, and I have five new arrows which my father made for me."

"I will come with you to blow the turkey calls," Pocahontas offered quickly. She badly wanted to go hunting herself. Often she thought the boys and men in her land had more fun than their sisters.

Walking softly, the two children went off, away from the noisy camp. Their bright eyes searched each bush and each open place between the trees.

Pocahontas lifted to her lips a little tube about as long as her hand. It was made of the bone of a wild turkey wing. With one hand held half over her mouth, the girl knew just how to blow the call of a wild turkey through it.

"Look! A turkey is there, down the path!" she said softly to Little Wolf.

At the sound of her call, a huge wild turkey had stepped out of the bushes. The great bird cocked his head, first on one side, then on the other.

From her hiding place behind a tree, Pocahontas gave another low call on the little bone tube. The bird slowly walked a few paces nearer. Then he stood still again, looking and looking for another bird.

Little Wolf took aim. His arrow flew straight.

"Your arrow, too, has eyes to see the way, Little Wolf," Pocahontas cried when they lifted the still turkey up off the ground.

That night, and each night of the Great Hunt, there was feasting in the Powhatans' camp. Deer meat and wild turkeys were roasted on clean chunks of hard wood. Always, bits of the best meat were offered to Manito. Then two hundred hungry people ate until they could eat no more.

Pocahontas had all the deer liver she wanted, and juicy deer tongues as well. These were the parts of a freshly killed deer which she liked the best.

After the feasting, happy songs rang through the western wilderness. Under the round moon, the hunters danced to show their joy and to give thanks to Manito for their good hunting.

The Great Deer Hunt

At last they had killed enough deer to feed and clothe every family. The meat all was cut up and much had been smoked. The deerskins had been washed and their inner sides were scraped clean.

The Great Deer Hunt was over!

In the Time of the Co-honks

"*Co-honk! Co-honk! Co-honk! Co-honk!*"

The quiet of the Indian town of Werowocomico was broken by the cries of the wild geese flying south. Looking up at the gray sky, Pocahontas could see the great V made by the bodies of hundreds of birds.

The Time of the Co-honks had come. Winter was here, and the wise birds were winging their way to the warm southland.

So many geese were flying there across the heavens that it took them a full half day to pass. More came with each sunrise.

Pocahontas and her friends liked to watch the wild geese, especially when they dropped down to rest and to feed on the near-by marshes. The wild celery and oats that grew in the marshes were their favorite foods. The children thought the wings of the geese

In the Time of the Co-honks

sounded like thunder when they beat the air to rise up into the sky again.

"It is good that all our birds do not fly away south when the cold comes," Pocahontas often said. It was nice to see the small scarlet cardinals, and the bigger bluejays on the bare brown limbs of the trees. And the red-headed woodpecker, furiously digging insects out of old tree trunks, made a friendly tapping sound in the still forest.

Bears had curled up inside their dens for their winter sleep. Rabbits and squirrels were snug in their tree holes. Turkeys and deer were hard to find now. Hunters often came home with no fresh meat at all. And even the fish were hid away under the ice on the edges of the rivers. No wonder the Powhatans called their winter The Hungry Time.

The season of the Co-honks seemed long in this year of 1607. But life in Werowocomico went on, day by day, much as it had in other years.

"I can stay in the cold water longer than you," the children cried to each other as they dived into the icy river each morning.

"No, today I shall stay longest."

"No, me!"

"No, it will be me!" Each one wanted to show how brave he was. He knew if he came out too soon, the others would run after him and pull him back into the water.

Tingling after her morning dip, Pocahontas ran about until she was dry. Then she threw on her warm mantle of soft muskrat-skins. The furry robe fell to her knees. In very cold weather, she pulled on her high leggings made of tanned deerskins.

The Indian girl liked to make the rounds of the wigwams to see what was going on. There was always plenty to do and plenty to see in her busy town.

In every wigwam the women, and the men, too, were hard at work. The men were making arrows, fishhooks, or hunting spears. The women were weaving baskets or arrow cases; making clay pots and bowls; or sewing the deerskins from the Great Deer Hunt into mantles, skirts, leggings, or moccasins. Or, perhaps, they were bent over their cooking fires stirring corn soup, or deer meat and turkey stew.

"Today, my brother, Nantakas, is having a weasel tattooed on his arm," Pocahontas told one of her friends on a cold winter morning. And the two girls ran to the wigwam of Big Tree, the tattoomaker.

Big Tree had already begun his work. With the sharp tooth of a fish, he was pricking the skin on the young man's arm. The girls knew this must hurt. But they would have been surprised if Nantakas had shown any sign that he felt the painful bite of the fish tooth.

With each prick, a tiny hole was made in the young man's skin. With prick after prick, Big Tree made the outline of a small weasel. When the holes were all made, the old tattoo artist rubbed heavy black powder over his picture.

"It is a fine weasel," Nantakas said when the bleeding had stopped. All the blood and loose black powder were now washed away. All that was left on his arm was the clear outline of the animal, made by black dots.

"It is a very fine weasel," Pocahontas agreed. "Now, my brother, wherever you are, your guardian animal will always be with you."

The next wigwam the girls entered was the home of the grandmother of Pocahontas, the mother of her own mother. On this morning the old woman was working upon a fine feather-cloth mantle for Pocahontas herself.

"I have finished the red cardinal, Little Snow Feather," the old woman said, smiling. She held up a large square of soft cloth, made mostly of the little feathers from wild-turkey breasts.

So cleverly had the woman fastened the feathers into the woven net underneath them, that no bit of its silk grass thread could be seen. One saw only the feathers, dark feathers and light feathers, all put together to make a pretty design.

"The redbird is beautiful, grandmother." Pocahontas smiled as she looked at her new feather mantle. She ran her fingers across the little redbird which had been worked into its front.

"It's the prettiest feather cloak in all Werowocomico," she cried happily. "And it will keep me so warm."

On her way out of her grandmother's wigwam, Pocahontas spied her father coming back from the river. Running to him, she threw her arms about his waist. She looked up into his face with love in her eyes. She was fond of her old father for all he was so stern and so cruel to his enemies and to wrongdoers.

"I shall come with you to comb your hair, my dear father," she cried. And she danced along by the old Chief's side into the wigwam.

"Shall I pull out those hairs on your chin, my father?" she asked, when the old man was seated on his wood couch at the end of the wigwam. "I have a good clamshell nipper. I will be gentle and quick. It shall not hurt." Pocahontas held up a small closed clam-shell. The Powhatan men thought such a clam-shell made a good pair of tweezers to pull hairs off their faces.

"No," Powhatan smiled. "I shall leave the hairs on my chin today. But you may comb out my scalp lock. Then you may bring me a bowl of good stew. I am hungry after my swim."

In the Time of the Co-honks

Pocahontas sat on the couch, close beside her father. Patiently, she waited until he had finished his eating. When he lay back on the soft skins of the couch, she began to speak.

"The white Manitos leave the hairs on their chins. Thunder Eagle says so. Did you ever see the white tribe from over the wide waters? Are they tall? Or are they short? What are they like, those strange pale-faced men?"

"They are tall, so say the people who have seen them." Powhatan did not answer the girl's questions directly. "Their faces truly are pale. Thunder Eagle is right. And most of them do not pull the hairs out of their chins.

"Some have dark hair and beards. Others have hair the color of copper or gold. Some have dark eyes. Others have eyes of light gray or blue.

"Their clothes are not like our own deerskins. Their ways, too, are different. The words the pale-faced tribe speak are not like those of any tribe in this land.

"But why should this not be so, Little Snow Feather? The Great Spirit, who made us all, has powerful medicine. Why should he have to make all men after the same pattern?

"The birds and the beasts are not all of one kind. Some walk on four legs. Some creep on the ground. Some wear fur. Some wear feathers. And the fish that swim in the water have neither feathers nor fur.

"Manito has the magic to give men pale skins, as well as copper-colored skins like our own. He teaches one tribe to make one kind of clothes. Another tribe makes clothes of a different kind."

"Do you fear the white Manitos, Great One?" Pocahontas asked then. "Do you think they will ever come in their winged boats here to our river?"

"No, Little Snow Feather, I do not fear the white strangers from over the sea. Perhaps one day they will come up the Pamunkey."

"What would you do, Wahunsonacock, if the white men should come here to Werowocomico? What would you do if they set up their wigwams here as they did in the lands to the south?"

"Our country is large, my daughter. The Great Spirit has given us vast forests and deep rivers. There are deer for many people. There are more fish in the rivers than we can eat. There is enough food here for us and the white visitors, too.

"If the white-skinned men come as friends, we shall receive them as friends. If they come as enemies, they shall feel the bite of our arrows and the sting of our hunting spears.

"My lookouts keep watch all along the shores of our Great Salt Water Bay. By day and by night, they look across the wide waters. They will tell us in time if the strange boats with wings come. Do not fear, Little

Snow Feather! Those pale-faced people shall do you no harm."

"O, I do not fear the white Manitos, my father," Pocahontas spoke quickly. "I want them to come. I want to see them for myself. I think I shall like to have them for my friends."

PART TWO

New Friends and Foes

The White Strangers Come

A BABY deer stood on its wobbly legs in the middle of the small pen which the children had made for it. Running Fox and Little Wolf had helped Pocahontas pound the slender sticks deep into the ground. Other friends had brought strong grapevines to weave in and out between the sticks to hold them together.

The fawn was a fine new pet, Pocahontas thought. Her baby raccoon was old enough now to have babies herself. Long since, the little creature had escaped into the deep woods. Pocahontas always was hoping to see her coon bringing her own little ones out of their home in some hollow tree.

It was the Time of the Blossoms. The wild-cherry and plum trees had put on their bright spring mantles. Amid the darker evergreens, the dogwood trees and the red buds were like white and pink clouds. The ground was covered with green May apple leaves. Purple violets and other spring flowers were everywhere.

The wild geese, the cranes, and the ducks had gone north again. The Moon of the Shad was past. Spring was blowing its warm sweet breath over the land.

When the first bits of green showed on the bare brown tree branches, the Werowocomico women had planted their corn. Each day, now, the men went forth to fish and to hunt. It was Powhatan himself who that day had brought home this baby fawn.

The Indian boys and girls were admiring the pen they had made, and they were stroking the soft coat of the little deer. Suddenly they heard a great noise down by the river, and in the town itself.

Women were calling. Men were shouting. A crowd was running along beside a messenger who had just brought his canoe to the landing place.

"What is it? What is it?" the children cried as they ran off to find out what the noise meant.

"The white strangers! The white strangers!" The messenger had no breath to say more as he ran towards Powhatan's wigwam.

"The white strangers? The white strangers?" The people repeated his words with fear and wonder in their hearts.

The White Strangers Come

"The Pale-Faced Ones from across the wide salt waters are here!" The runner panted when at last he stood before the wood porch where The Powhatan sat, enjoying the spring sunshine.

"By the smoke fires, we have had the news from our brothers at the mouth of the Great Salt Water Bay. With their own eyes there, they have seen the strangers' canoes move up into our Powhatan River."

"When? How many? Tell it quickly!" Powhatan spoke urgently. But then he remembered the custom of his people. "Bring food for this messenger," he called to his wives. "He is hungry. He must eat."

"Two sleeps ago, the Pale-Faced Ones came, Wahunsonacock. We have brought you the word as fast as we could. The white strangers have come in three giant canoes. Each boat is as big as The Powhatan's wigwam. Ten times ten and more is the number of the Pale Faces. And they are like none of the tribes in this land.

"The strangers' giant canoes have great gray wings above them, and they fly before the wind. Over the eastern ocean, they have come, just as our forefathers told it."

Silence fell over the crowd gathered there before Powhatan. People looked at each other. None knew what to think.

What was this man saying? Were these pale-faced

visitors sent here by the Great Spirit? Were they Manitos themselves? Would they be the friends of the Powhatans? Or would they be foes?

Powhatan also was silent, but it never occurred to Pocahontas that he was afraid. Her own heart was beating and beating. In her excitement, her new pet was forgotten. All she could think was, "They have come! They have come! The white Manitos have come!"

"Speak on, man!" Powhatan commanded. "How did the strangers greet the people of our wigwams? Are they friends? Or are they enemies?"

"They made signs of friendship. They gave presents to those who gathered along the river to meet them. And they spoke with happy voices when they walked on our land. No one could understand their strange words, but they smiled and they laughed. Our people smiled, too."

"That is good!" The Powhatan nodded his head.

"But the smiles did not last, Wahunsonacock. At night, when the Pale-Faced Ones were on their way back to their canoes, arrows flew out of the bushes upon them. Not all our people trusted these strangers. Our arrows wounded two of the Pale Faces. And all the others were angry.

"They brought forth their magic fire-tubes which

The White Strangers Come

have voices like thunder. Their magic can kill a bird high in the sky, or an enemy far, far away.

"It is no wonder that our brothers ran to hide in the woods. It is not strange, either, that the noise of the fire-tubes made all in that place run away from their wigwams.

"When the white men came to their village, their fire holes were still warm. There were pots of smoked oysters still cooking upon them. But no man or woman was there."

"I know the magic of the white stranger's guns. It is bad medicine for their enemies." Powhatan no doubt was thinking of earlier days in the southland.

"It is better that these visitors should be treated as friends," he said thoughtfully. "If we do not make them angry, no doubt they will go away. They have come here before. But they have not stayed.

"Go along the river," The Powhatan ordered his runners. "Pass the word to all the weroances to make these strangers their brothers. And every day let the word be brought to me here, telling what the Pale Faces do."

Pocahontas could hardly wait until news came again. She kept close to the wigwam. When the next runner arrived, she sat just behind Powhatan where she could hear every word.

"The giant canoes with wings are now far up the Powhatan River," this messenger reported. "The strangers are looking and looking over our country. They lay their hands over their hearts to show they want to be friends. Presents come out of their canoes at each stopping place. Every weroance on the river begs them to visit his village."

"And where are these three giant canoes with the gray wings?" The Powhatan broke his silence.

"They rest in the deep stream which cuts through the point of land which lies between the Pamunkey and the Powhatan Rivers." With a sharp stick, the messenger drew on the ground the outline of this peninsula near the mouth of Chesapeake Bay.

Powhatan nodded. He understood why the white strangers thought this deep, sheltered stream would be a good harbor. Canoes were safe there from the storms that swept up the Bay.

"The white men's iron tomahawks have strong magic." There was admiration and wonder in the messenger's words.

"They cut down the forest trees far more quickly than we can by our burning and scraping with our tools of stone. Already these strangers have cleared places for their shelters. Already their blankets are spread over their house frames, made of young trees.

"The strangers have paid for their camping place.

At first the weroances welcomed the Pale Faces in their giant canoes with wings.

The White Strangers Come

In exchange they have given bells, beads, and copper, and many other fine gifts.

"The Pale Faces call their camp village 'James Town.' They call our Powhatan River the 'James River.' 'James' is the name of their king. And 'England' is their country across the wide waters."

The Powhatan was silent. He was thinking and thinking what he should do.

"We shall double the guards here at Werowocomico. We must know always where these strangers go and what they do. Their village of James Town on the Powhatan River is not far from our wigwams here. It is only a few hours' swift running from Werowocomico."

Each day Nantakas and other young braves crossed the Pamunkey River, then ran through the forest to watch the newcomers. Each day they brought a new tale back to The Powhatan.

Pocahontas said nothing to The Powhatan before she made her first journey to the new village of James Town. She feared her father would say that she could not go. And she badly wanted to see the white Manitos with her own eyes.

White Owl and Little Wolf went along with her. From a safe distance, well hidden in the trees, the young Indians had their first sight of the strange men from over the sea.

"How furry their hair is! How hairy are their faces! What strange clothing they wear! Their coats must be made of the skins of wild beasts which we never have seen." White Owl spoke softly lest he be overheard. These Indians knew nothing of cloth.

"Their eyes are so pale and so round. With their white skins, these strangers look sick and weak. I think they are ugly." Little Wolf did not like the looks of the white men.

"Their faces are bright as the sun," Pocahontas declared. "I like their wide-open eyes and their quick ways. Their mouths often smile. They look friendly and kind. Someday I shall go closer to these white strangers. Perhaps I shall even talk to them!" The Powhatan's daughter did not lack courage.

Of all the men she watched that day, Pocahontas admired most the one whom the others called Captain John Smith. His ruddy hair and beard shone like copper. His blue eyes were bright. He stood so straight, and his steps were so sure.

Pocahontas picked John Smith out easily wherever he was. He always seemed to be telling the other men what to do. Surely, he must be one of their weroances.

An Okee Falls in Battle

"*Wingapoh!* We are friends!" said the two white weroances, Captain Newport and Captain John Smith.

"*Wingapoh!*" said The Powhatan. He laid his hand over his heart in sign that he would take these Englishmen for his brothers.

With some twenty companions, the two leaders of the new settlement at James Town were exploring the Powhatan River. Their barge had moved far up this great stream.

Indians guided the strangers. With pointed sticks, they drew little maps on the ground, to show the windings of the river.

Often, the Indians who lived along the Powhatan River brought their visitors deer meat and fish, roasted corn, purple mulberries and juicy wild strawberries. They were pleased with the knives, the needles, the beads, and the bells they received in return for their gifts of food.

Captain Newport and Captain John Smith had landed that day at the little town of Powhatan far up the river. They were just presenting a hatchet to the weroance of that place when there was a shout.

"The Powhatan comes. It is The Powhatan himself!"

The people of the village gathered to salute their mighty Weroance-of-Weroances. And the white men watched curiously while the old Chief and his guard marched through the corn fields and tobacco patches, and up the hill to the village.

Captain John Smith and Captain Newport hastened to speak their words of friendship. And they were glad when they heard The Powhatan answer their greeting with *"Wingapoh!"*

It was not their first meeting with the king of this land. Once before, farther down the river, he had also paid them a visit.

This time they feasted together and smoked the peace pipe. As a sign of his love for his English brothers, The Powhatan laid his own raccoon skin mantle on the shoulders of Captain Newport.

The white visitors invited their Indian hosts to share a feast of their own on the edge of the river.

An Okee Falls in Battle

Their roasted pork was a new dish to these Indians whose only meat came from the wild beasts of the forest.

"We would like to go far, far up this river," the white chiefs said to The Powhatan when the feasting was over. "We seek the great ocean which may lie beyond."

"I do not believe there is an ocean beyond the hills. And boats cannot go farther than the high waterfalls in the river." The Powhatan shook his head.

"But some say there may be an ocean there," Captain Newport insisted. "If we cannot go there by boat, we will walk over the land. We will carry our canoes until we come to that great salt water sea.

"The land is rough. The hills are high. There is no food. And the way is long." Powhatan still discouraged their journey into the west. "But if you must go, I will give you guides."

"The white strangers shouted a friendly farewell when my canoe went down the river," The Powhatan smiled as he remembered. "We waved our deerskin mantles above our heads and shouted farewell to them. It was good that we were friends."

The Indians were not surprised when the weary explorers soon returned, without finding the great ocean they sought. Their canoes were much too heavy to carry very far over the mountains.

Many Indians along the river followed The Powhatan's example of friendship for the newcomers. Sometimes shooting targets were set up. The white men admired the Indians' skill with their bows and arrows. The Indians were amazed to see how far the white men could shoot with their guns.

At the thunder of the guns, they covered their ears. Some jumped from their canoes and fled into the forest. They did not feel safe until Captain John Smith explained that he used these guns only to punish his enemies.

Other Indians, however, like Opekankano, the weroance of the Pamunkey Tribes, did not quite trust the white strangers. Opekankano's lands along the Pamunkey River to the north were rich in game and in corn fields. He showed his visitors great baskets of corn, rich furs, and mussel pearls. This Pamunkey weroance was second in importance only to his powerful brother, The Powhatan.

The Indian promises of friendship did not last long. When Captain Newport and Captain John Smith returned to James Town, bad news awaited them.

"We were working on our houses," their friends told them. "We were busy in our corn fields. Suddenly, without warning, Indian arrows flew through the air like a great swarm of hornets.

"One arrow went through the whiskers of Captain

An Okee Falls in Battle

Wingfield. Others wounded seventeen of our men. One boy was killed.

"We ran for our guns. We shot off the cannon upon our ship. The Indians felt its fire, for a great branch crashed down upon their hiding place. It made them all run away."

The only protection the new village then had consisted of a few tree branches piled up in a half circle before it. Now a tall, strong fence of young tree trunks was built all the way round it. The tree trunks were set so close together that Indian arrows could not get through.

The bushes and tall grass around the camp were cut down. No Indian now could creep close without being seen. Cannons were brought ashore off the boats, and kept always ready. The men of James Town took turns watching for unfriendly visitors.

The hot summer of 1607 was a bad time for the settlers. The near-by marshes were damp. They were filled with mosquitoes which spread fevers that made men very ill.

Worse still, the settlers did not have enough to eat. Their corn had been planted too late. The wheat and barley they had brought with them had been spoiled by the five months' journey over the ocean. The Englishmen did not know how to hunt and fish nearly so well as the Indians did.

"*Wingapoh!*" Captain John Smith said to the Indians he met during his trading trips on the rivers. Now that Captain Newport had taken the ships back over the sea for more food and more men, John Smith was in charge of the James Town settlement.

"Give us corn, deer meat, and fish! And you shall have beads, bells, and axes," he said to the weroances.

But many of the Indians only laughed at their hungry visitors. Among themselves, they said, "If we do not give these men food, they will have to go back to their own land."

To Captain John Smith, one weroance said: "Give us two of your long knives. Then we will give you a whole basket of corn and a big turkey as well."

The long shining swords of the white men were the treasures which the Indians wanted most. These sharp steel blades could cut down an enemy much more quickly than their own swords made of wood. It was because of their swords that the Powhatans often spoke of these Englishmen as the "Long Knives."

"Two fine swords for only one small basket of corn! And only one turkey!" Captain John Smith was angry.

"The Indians make fun of us," he declared to the five companions who were with him on the barge. "Our people are starving. We must have food. If kind words will not get us food from the Indians, then our guns must speak."

The Indians felt sure of themselves that day. Only

An Okee Falls in Battle

six men rode in the white men's barge, while they were many, many times that small number.

So they were surprised when the barge moved in close to the river bank. At the first thunderbolts from their visitors' guns, they ran like frightened deer, off into the deep woods.

Boldly, John Smith and his little band ran after the Indians. Loudly and angrily, the Englishmen's thunder-tubes spoke again and again.

When they came to the village, no Indian was to be seen. But there was corn in the storehouses, and other food, too.

"Here is enough corn to fill our barge many times," his men said to Captain John Smith. They would have started for the river with the baskets of yellow ears. But John Smith said, "No."

"We shall have arrows in our backs before we can reach the barge," he warned them. "The Indians are only waiting for the right moment. We must watch, with our guns ready."

And he was right. A great band of Indians soon came dancing and prancing out of the forest. They were painted for war: black, white, red, and blue.

Held high, they carried their Okee before them. The air was filled with flying arrows from their bent bows. They shouted their shrill war cry. They were sure of a victory.

Powhatan nodded his head when this story was told to him. Pocahontas, sitting close by, could see in her mind the deerskin-covered image of the terrible Okee. With its ugly, painted face, with its necklaces of copper and pearls, bird claws and bear's teeth, an Okee was strong medicine in time of war. It was strange that these Long Knives did not run away.

"Our people had war clubs. They had swords, bows, and arrows," the runner went on with his story. "But the white men had their thunder-tubes and their long knives. Our thickest bark shields did not stop the thunderbolts from their guns. The magic of the Okee did not dull the blades of their swords.

"One after another, our warriors fell. The Okee fell, too. None of our braves had time to save the Okee as they ran away into the woods."

Pocahontas shivered at this point in the story. Powhatan's face was troubled. "Go on! What happened next?"

"The white weroance sent a message to our weroance. A prisoner who was only wounded a little, carried the word. The white weroance said six of our men without war clubs or swords, without bows and arrows, should go into the village. They should fill his barge full of corn. Then our Okee would come back to us. Beads, copper, and hatchets would pay us a fair price for the corn. The prisoners, then, would go free."

"Captain John Smith was kind," Pocahontas said to

her father. "His men had won the battle. He had many prisoners. He had even captured the Okee. He could have taken all the corn without any pay."

The Powhatan nodded his head slowly. "Aye, to be friends with these Long Knives is the better way. It is not good to make war on this tribe to whom the Great Spirit has given such magic weapons."

With its ugly painted face, an Okee was strong medicine in time of war.

"Perhaps the strangers will go away of themselves, when the giant canoes come again from over the sea." The old Chief spoke hopefully.

"It is this same Captain John Smith who keeps the Long Knives here in our land," Nantakas told his father. "Many of the men of James Town have died. Others are ill. All are hungry. Some would have gone away before now in the one canoe which Captain Newport left here behind him. But Captain John Smith learned of the plan. He fired his great thunderbolts across the boat's path. And so they dared not go."

More and more, the Indians felt unhappy about these strangers in their land. It was plain to all, now, that they had come to stay.

A Wizard Is Captured

"BIG news, Great Weroance, I bring big news!" A messenger from far up the river spoke these words in The Powhatan's wigwam one cold winter day in the year 1608.

The old Chief raised himself on his fur-covered couch until he was sitting upright on its edge. Pocahontas, who had been weaving a reed basket in the smoky light of the wigwam fire, put down her work. She came close to listen.

"Your brother, Opekankano, and his Pamunkey tribe have captured the white weroance, Captain John Smith," the messenger cried.

"Captain John Smith is captured?" Pocahontas could hardly believe that this bold white Manito could ever be taken.

"So it is, truly. For all he is a wizard, for all his strong magic, the white Manito is now a prisoner of the Pamunkeys in the town of Orapax."

The Powhatan's dark eyes shone. Whether he was pleased or displeased at the great news, Pocahontas could not tell.

"Say how it was, man!" the old Chief commanded. "Opekankano has long been wanting a war with the Long Knives. Opekankano does not believe the Pale Faces are truly our friends. Tell me just how it was that the wizard was taken."

And this is the happening of which that messenger told the Powhatan king.

Opekankano and his braves were hunting in the Chickahominy River country. Hundreds of them were hunting together there. And word came that the barge from James Town was moving up the Chickahominy River towards their hunting ground.

Some said Captain John Smith and his little band of men were trading for corn. Others said they were still seeking the ocean which they hoped to find in the west.

When Opekankano came upon the Englishmen's barge, John Smith was not in it. The boat was pulled up onto the river bank. And the men who had been left to guard it had gone with their Indian guide into the forest.

A Wizard Is Captured

At the sound of the first war whoop, the white men ran for their boat. All but one reached it safely. But that one was captured by Opekankano's braves.

With tomahawks raised to strike, the Pamunkeys forced the terrified man to tell where his leader had gone.

"Up the river! In a little canoe!" the trembling coward cried out. That white stranger was truly not a brave man. He could not bear the bite of a hatchet or the pricking of arrow points.

"How many others are with Captain John Smith?" Opekankano asked then.

"Two of us went with him. And two Indian guides. Now, I have told. Let me go to my boat!" The man almost screamed, so great was his fear.

"It is enough!" Opekankano declared. He nodded to his warriors. And their hatchets and arrows quickly ended the life of the miserable fellow.

The small exploring party from James Town had gone twenty long miles up the Chickahominy River. The white men were tired. They had had to carry their canoe over the rocky parts of the stream and across fallen logs. They were glad when they pulled the canoe up on the river bank to camp for the night.

Captain John Smith had left his two white companions there to watch for unfriendly Indians. "Fire a shot from your guns to warn us if there is an attack," he told these two men. And then he said to his two

Powhatan guides, "You shall come with me into the woods to hunt a turkey for our supper."

But the two men, making the campfire, did not have time to fire a warning shot. Too quickly came the arrows from the unfriendly Pamunkeys. The good Captain never saw his two English friends alive again.

The wilderness rang with the war whoops of the Pamunkeys when they caught up with Captain John Smith. The white weroance was brave, so the runner told Powhatan and Pocahontas. Alone, he fought off the attack of the hundreds of Pamunkey braves. Two of their number were killed by the magic bolts from his thunder-tube. Many others were wounded.

Arrows hung from John Smith's clothing, their points caught in the cloth. But, as if by some magic, he received only one wound, just a slight wound in his hip.

The fearless Captain held one of his Indian guides between himself and his foes. With his garter, he bound the young Powhatan tightly to his left arm. Holding the Indian before him as a shield, Smith backed, slowly and slowly, towards his canoe.

Light snow covered the ground. John Smith could not know that in places, beneath the white snow, that river bank was a sea of soft mud. One more backward step, and he felt himself sinking into the marsh. His guide was sinking with him. They were caught and held fast in the mud up to their waists.

A Wizard Is Captured

The circle of Indians crept closer, their bows and their arrows held in their hands. But they did not shoot for fear of the white man's thunder-tube.

Soon, however, Captain John Smith felt the winter chill of the icy mud creeping up through his body. His two legs were as numb as if he were already dead.

"I will throw down my gun, if they will give me my life," he cried to his guide. Through the Indian, he made Opekankano understand that he would surrender.

The Indians pulled the two men out of the marsh. They took the half-frozen Captain back to their campfire. And they rubbed his numb legs until once more he could feel the warm blood flowing into them.

How happy was that weroance, Opekankano! What a great victory was this for his Pamunkey tribe!

His braves rejoiced, too. They made ready to tie their prisoner to a tree. They fitted their arrows to their bows. It was plain to Captain John Smith that they meant to kill him at once.

What would save him? The white weroance called on his magic, or so the Indians told it. Out of his pocket he drew a strange little box. It was of smoothest white bone, bone far finer than any the Pamunkeys ever had seen. Elephant ivory was not found here in their land of America.

Inside the small box, there was a tiny splinter of

iron. And, wonder of wonders, the iron splinter moved back and forth and around, all by itself.

Powhatan and Pocahontas sat silent and puzzled when the messenger told how the tiny iron splinter moved inside the bone box. They could not understand a compass any better than could Opekankano and his men, who had held it in their own hands.

What made the bit of iron move? And why could the Pamunkey chief not touch it with his fingertip? None of the Indians had ever seen thin glass used as a box lid. Surely this box was some strong magic charm.

And what did the white wizard mean when he said the iron splinter always would point to the North Star? How could a trinket like this, except by some magic, help these white Manitos find their way over the wide salt waters of the ocean?

"Stop!" Opekankano called to his warriors when they raised their bows to shoot. "This man is surely a wizard. Who knows what he can do with this magic charm?" The Pamunkey Chief held the ivory compass box high so that all could see it.

"Let us not kill him yet! Untie him from the tree, but guard him well. We shall take him with us to Orapax."

In triumph, the Pamunkeys marched into the village with their great prize. Opekankano led the way, and his warriors followed him in single file. Three tall Pamunkeys walked close to the pris-

A Wizard Is Captured

oner, one on each side and one at his back. Six others with drawn bows, and arrows in place, marched on each side.

The people of Orapax came running to see the strange sight. The women and girls, the old men and boys, too, stood close to stare at the very first white man they ever had seen.

That night, there was dancing because of their victory. The Pamunkeys' faces and shoulders were red with puccoon paint. Stuffed birds, with wings spread, adorned their heads. Strings of copper and white beads, and rattles from grandfather snakes hung at their necks and their wrists.

The braves leaped and they danced. They sang and they yelled. Not until three victory dances had been danced did they stop celebrating the capture of the white wizard.

Forty men guarded Captain John Smith inside the long wigwam, where a fine supper was served to him. Platters of food were set down before him as he rested there by the fire. A great weroance such as this one should not go hungry, even though he must die when the feasting was done.

Powhatan's runner told also how one Indian brought Captain John Smith a fur mantle to keep off the cold of the winter night. This was in exchange, he said, for some bells and other trinkets which Smith had once given him.

Pocahontas was glad the Pamunkeys had been kind to their noble prisoner. She so much wanted her people to be friends with these pale-faced visitors from over the sea.

"What shall be done with the white wizard," the Pamunkeys asked Opekankano. "Shall we not kill him before he brings harm upon us?"

"If this man is truly one of his Manitos, the Great Spirit would be angry. The Powhatan would be angry, too. The Powhatan wishes to make the Long Knives his friends. Let the white wizard live yet for a little while!"

"My people would like to see this white wizard," said one of the less important chiefs of the Pamunkeys.

"My people should see the white wizard, too," another from a distant village declared.

"Good! We shall make the rounds of the villages with this prisoner," Opekankano replied. "So we shall show our people that the medicine of the Pamunkeys is even stronger than that of the white Manitos."

The Charm That Talked

THE next messenger from Chickahominy country had another story about Captain John Smith to tell Powhatan and Pocahontas.

Their noble prisoner soon made friends with the Pamunkey Indians. They liked his twinkling blue eyes and his merry laugh. They liked it that this Long Knife weroance did not seem afraid. And they liked his strange tales.

The white weroance had, by now, learned many Indian words. With these, and with signs, he could make his Indian captors understand him.

Opekankano sat with Captain John Smith by the fire in the Chief's wigwam in Orapax, safe from the cold of the winter weather outside. Eagerly he listened to his prisoner's tales of the giant ships which had brought the white Manitos across the wide waters.

How the great boats were made of slices of tree trunks, fastened together, and how their cracks were sealed tight! How their wings, which the Captain called sails, were pushed along by the winds! How, by watching the sun, the moon, and the stars, the sailors found their way over the ocean! And how, when the heavens were covered with clouds, the magic compass could tell them where to go!

Opekankano thought for a long time about the things Captain John Smith told him.

"This man knows much which we do not know," he told his people. "He has strong magic which we do not understand. We shall do well not to offend him."

Not all the Pamunkeys felt so friendly towards their prisoner, however. One day, while Captain John Smith talked with his guard, an Indian rushed in with his war club raised high. He would have killed the white prisoner if the guards had not caught his arm just in time.

"This man is the father of a young brave who was wounded by your thunder-tube at the edge of the river," the guard said to the Captain. "His son now is dying and, for that, he seeks to kill you."

"Perhaps I can cure his son," John Smith replied.

But when the Indians took him to the wigwam where the dying youth lay, he shook his head. "I cannot heal such a wound without medicine which is in

The Charm That Talked

my own house at James Town. Let me go there to fetch it, and it may be I can save the young man."

But Opekankano suspected that his prisoner also thought this journey might give him a chance to escape. So he said, "No."

Later, however, the Pamunkey Chief came to his captive and said, "You shall go to James Town, Captain John Smith, if you will go there with us and help us to attack it. We Pamunkeys shall be three hundred strong. We shall have our tomahawks and our swords, and our bows and our arrows. We shall come in the night when the Long Knives are asleep.

"Help us in the attack, Captain John Smith, and you shall go free. We shall give you a part of this land for your own. You shall choose as many Indian wives as you wish. When James Town is destroyed, we shall call you our brother and make you a weroance of our tribe."

"You can never destroy James Town, Opekankano," Captain John Smith replied. "Thunderbolts will fly out of the great guns. Our magic will open the ground under your feet." Captain John Smith now was speaking of the gunpowder mines which had been laid in the earth around the little fort.

"We do not believe such things can happen!" the Indian chief cried. "Even white wizards cannot work wonders like these."

"Send three of your braves down the river to

James Town. Let them look on these wonders with their own eyes. Let them tell my brothers there that the Pamunkeys treat their white prisoner with kindness. My brothers will be glad to know that I still live."

"If your brothers know you are alive, they will come seeking you, and there will be war," Opekankano objected. "My messengers shall go down the river to James Town. They shall look at these wonders. But they shall say nothing about you to your brothers."

Captain John Smith thought for a moment. Then he spoke thus: "If you say they shall not, then your messengers need not speak of me. And I will give them a charm to keep the men of James Town from doing them harm."

John Smith took from his pocket a little notebook. He brought forth a small tin bottle filled with black ink. And with his knife, he cut the end of a wild goose's quill into a sharp point.

First he dipped the quill into the tin bottle. With it, he made black marks on a paper page which he tore out of his notebook.

The Indians marveled at the paper. This strange object was no thicker than the leaf of a tulip poplar tree. They wondered at its whiteness. It was even whiter than the whitest bark of the birch tree.

The Charm That Talked

"Let your braves make signs of friendship when they come to the fort," said Captain John Smith. "Let them show my brothers this charm so that they may return safely. Or let them lay the charm down on the tree stump near the gate of the fort.

"My white brothers will find it there. Then, they will fire the great guns but without harm to your men. Before your messengers' eyes, my brothers will open the earth.

"My brothers will give your messengers clothing to replace my coat and my breeches which were so badly torn by your Pamunkey arrows. They will give them dry shoes to replace mine which were spoiled when I fell into the marsh. They will also give the messengers a sharp hatchet, white beads, and other fine presents for their great chief, Opekankano."

The Pamunkeys marveled. They did not understand how any of these things could happen unless the messengers talked of Captain John Smith.

Opekankano looked at the black marks which his prisoner had made on the magic charm. In them, he found no pictures of a white man or Indian captors. There were no pictures of the sun to tell how many days' march the messengers had come. There was no winding river to show they were from up the Chickahominy.

The Indian chief had no way of knowing what

Smith had written on the leaf from his notebook. The only writing Opekankano knew was by means of pictures or symbols.

He could not know that Smith had written the men of James Town of Opekankano's plot to attack their fort; that he had told his friends there to fire off the cannons, and set off a ground mine of gunpowder while the messengers watched. They could not read the list of articles he had asked to have sent back to him.

In spite of the winter cold with its snow and ice, the three young Pamunkeys set forth in their log canoe. They needed stout hearts to make this journey down the Chickahominy into the Powhatan River and on to the James Town fort of the white strangers.

In a few days they came back, all three safe and sound. And they reported to Opekankano the wonders they had seen.

"The white wizard spoke truly," they said. "The magic of the men of James Town is mighty. We Pamunkeys can never destroy them.

"We crept through the forest, softly, softly, so that no one could hear us." So the Indians told the story to Opekankano. "We held our arrows ready to shoot while we took the prisoner's charm to the tree stump by the gate of the fort.

"How could the white men know the charm was

The Charm That Talked

there? We saw no one watching us. Yet, when we were hid in the woods, they came to pick it up. We saw them bend their heads over it, one after another.

"Soon, all happened just as the white wizard foretold. The great guns spoke, with clouds of thick black smoke. Thunderbolts crashed among the icy branches of the trees beyond our hiding place. Giant branches fell like autumn leaves to the floor of the forest.

"Next, the earth opened up before our eyes. With a roar three times as loud as that of the thunder, a great hole was torn in the ground. Rocks and dirt filled the air. We ran for our lives deep into the woods.

"But the men of James Town followed us. They cried *'Wingapoh,'* and they made other signs of friendship. We remembered, then, how the white wizard had promised that his charm would keep us safe. So we let them come near.

"Wonder of wonders, Opekankano! The Long Knives brought us the coat and the breeches and the dry boots for Captain John Smith. They gave us the hatchet, the white beads, and other presents for Opekankano, just as the white wizard said they would do. Yet, we had said not a word to them that this man was alive and our prisoner here."

Opekankano and his Pamunkeys sat silent when the messengers had finished their strange tale. They looked at their smiling prisoner with troubled eyes

How could Captain John Smith know just what

would happen? How could his words travel through the deep woods and over the corn fields between them and James Town?

Who else could have told his brothers there that he was alive? That he wanted fresh clothing and dry shoes? It could only be that the magic charm had talked.

Now, more than ever, Opekankano was afraid to put his white visitor to death. He must wait until The Great Powhatan could tell him what to do.

"Here is a wizard such as never before has been known in our land." Opekankano said to his people. "All the Powhatan tribes should see him. All should be told the tale of his magic. Tomorrow, we shall set forth with the white wizard to make the rounds of our villages."

Pocahontas of the Brave Heart

"There he is! Nantakas, I see the white Manito! There, beside Opekankano in the first canoe!"

Pocahontas and her brother were in the crowd at the landing place when Opekankano brought his noble prisoner to Werowocomico. Runners had kept Powhatan informed. He knew every step of the journey which his brother, the Pamunkey weroance, had made with his pale-faced captive.

For three weeks the log canoes carrying Captain John Smith and his guards had been paddled up and down the rivers of this part of the country.

"In every village, the people crowd about the white prisoner," the runners reported. "The women and children bring him food. The weroances make him welcome. In every wigwam, there is talk about this friendly man. How he smiles! How he shows no fear!"

On this fifth day of January, 1608, Pocahontas was wearing her new feather robe with the redbird worked into its front. She had put spots of red puccoon paint on her face. Her best white shell earrings were in her ears. Chains of copper links and white mussel pearls hung round her neck and her wrists. She wanted to look her best when the white weroance was brought to Werowocomico.

The crowd shouted as Captain John Smith was led by his guards to the open space in the center of the little town. All had a chance to look at him well, while The Powhatan made ready to receive him in his wigwam. Their Weroance-of-all-Weroances, too, wanted to put on his finest regalia to impress his noble guest.

"The Long Knives' weroance is brave!" Nantakas said to his sister. "See how straight he stands! Like a pine tree! How bold are his looks! If he is afraid, no one can tell it."

"Truly, this Pale Face is good to look at," Pocahontas replied. "His smile is as bright as a summer sky." And she smiled shyly back at the blue-eyed prisoner, whose red-brown hair and beard were the color of copper.

"Hey-o!" A great shout rose to the roof poles when at last the prisoner was led into the presence of the

The Pamunkeys at last brought Captain John Smith before The Great Powhatan.

great Indian king. The old weroance received him in state, sitting upon his low couch at one end of the smoky wigwam.

The Powhatan's robe was made of raccoon skins, with tails hanging from it like so many tassels. The pearls in his necklace were gleaming white. A flat copper ornament shone on his breast, and a crown of eagle feathers adorned his gray head.

Two of his young wives sat beside The Powhatan. Their faces and their shoulders were colored bright red, and downy white bird feathers powdered their painted skin.

Around the walls of the wigwam stood two rows of tall Powhatan warriors. And behind them were many women and men, all eager to know what would happen next.

Pocahontas and Nantakas found places between the guards where they could see well. They stood there in silence, their hearts beating with excitement.

With the customary Indian hospitality, the Chief of all the Powhatan tribes welcomed Captain John Smith. For all this Pale Face was a prisoner, he too was a weroance. A mat was spread for him to sit upon. A Powhatan queen from Appomatuck was given the honor of bringing the water for washing the noble guest's hands. Another woman brought soft turkey breast feathers with which he might dry them. Still others brought forth food for the feast.

Then Opekankano began to speak. He told Powhatan of the capture of the white wizard on the edge of the Chickahominy River. He told how the white stranger's gun there had taken the lives of two of the Pamunkey braves who attacked him.

Pocahontas could hardly breathe now from excitement and dismay. A kill for a kill! This was the law of her land. If this shining white Manito had truly killed members of a Powhatan tribe, what now could save him from their anger?

Powhatan listened until the story was told. Then he called his headmen about him so that each should speak his mind.

At last the council was over. And Pocahontas heard her father speak the dreadful words, "This man must die. Bring forth the stones! He shall die by the tomahawks and the clubs."

"No, No!" she burst out, breaking through the guards and throwing herself upon her father's knees. "Do not kill the white Manito, my father. O, let him live!"

But, for once, Powhatan did not listen to his dear daughter's pleading. He pushed her away from him.

"I have spoken," he said in a cold voice. "The white man shall die, just as our braves died from the bolts from his thunder-tube! Bring forth the stones. Raise the tomahawks! And strike quickly!"

Tears fell from the dark eyes of the Indian girl. Again and again, she begged her father to spare the life of John Smith.

"Pocahontas has a brave heart," the watching Powhatans whispered to one another. "None in this land is there with so brave a heart. Who else would try to stay an order of The Powhatan? It is almost as if she defied the Great Spirit himself."

Nantakas held his sister by the arm while the guards dragged two flat stones to the center of the wigwam. Many brown hands held the prisoner when he was thrown to the ground. They placed his head squarely upon one of the stones.

"The white man has a brave heart, too," the watching Indians said. "Look! He does not tremble. His eyes are steady and without fear."

The tomahawks were raised. Powhatan was about to speak the word "Strike!" when Pocahontas broke away from her brother's grasp. With a cry, she darted out to the side of the prisoner. She knelt close to him and she shielded his head with her own.

"I claim this prisoner from death, Wahunsonacock! According to our custom, I claim him for my brother. I claim Captain John Smith as Yellow Bird claimed White Owl."

Truly, this girl did have a brave heart to speak so to the mighty Chief of all the Powhatan tribes. *Ai-i-i,* she was brave to lay her own head in the path of the tomahawks. But she was but following the custom of her own Powhatan people. She had some right on her side.

Powhatan's heart softened. He loved his dear daughter. He was proud of her bravery. Perhaps, also, he still thought that friendship was the better way to deal with the Long Knives.

"Then let it be so!" the old Chief said. "Set the prisoner free! He now belongs to Pocahontas. She has adopted him as her brother."

Pocahontas jumped to her feet and gave her hand to help her white brother to stand once again. Her dark eyes shone. Her gentle face was wreathed in happy smiles.

"He shall make me bells and beads," she cried.

"For me, he shall make arrows and tomahawks." Powhatan spoke as he would have spoken of any war prisoner who had been claimed for adoption into the tribe.

All that day, and the next, Pocahontas scarcely left the side of Captain John Smith. She helped serve him the roast deer meat and corn cakes at the feasting in Powhatan's wigwam. She watched him take his puff on the peace pipe which her father passed to him.

When they had smoked the peace pipe together, she was no longer afraid that her father would harm her new pale-faced brother.

There was much talk in the wigwam between The Powhatan and his white visitor.

"Why did the Long Knives come to our land?" the old Chief asked. "What do you want here?"

"We are looking for a way for our ships to reach the rich lands which we call The Indies," the Captain replied. "Now, we must sail across the vast eastern oceans. The journey takes many moons. We hope to find another and a shorter route over a western sea."

"Some say there are salt waters beyond our western mountains," The Powhatan spoke thoughtfully. "But if these are salt lakes, or an ocean, I do not know. I have not been there myself."

"We look for gold too," John Smith explained farther. "Gold is greatly prized in our own land. But, also, we want to trade with the Powhatans." The English Captain spoke politely. "We like your soft furs. Your great trees can be cut into wide boards for building houses in our country over the sea. And we like your beautiful land. It is a land of great plenty." Captain John Smith smiled as he thought of the fertile corn fields and the forests so full of deer. "There is food here for many, many more people than the Powhatans.

"We wish to live with you as brothers." The white

visitor's words were soft and persuading. "We will teach our Indian brothers to build board houses like ours. We will show them how to weave cloth for their garments. And we will tell them of our God and His Blessed Son."

"But our own ways of living satisfy us," The Powhatan said then. "Our wigwams keep out the rain. Our deerskins cover us from the cold. Our Great Spirit, The Manito, walks at our side. We do not need your God."

Pocahontas herself was never tired of listening to her new brother's talk. She did not understand all the things he told her about his land over the ocean. To her it was a country of magic and mystery. On that January afternoon in 1608 she never dreamed that, one day, she herself would cross the wide ocean to see its wonders with her own eyes.

"This morning they will adopt you into our tribe," Pocahontas told Captain John Smith the second day after his narrow escape from the tomahawks. She would have liked to go with him. But a girl could not join the procession which led him to the great wigwam in the deep woods.

Alone, there, Captain John Smith sat down on the reed mat spread by the wigwam fire. Perhaps he wondered if Pocahontas had spoken truly, when she said he was to be adopted into the tribe. Perhaps he thought, "Surely, now that they have brought me here, out of her sight, the Powhatans mean to kill me."

But he made no sign of his fears. He sat quiet even when the great noise began behind the reed curtain that divided the wigwam into two rooms. Voices shrieked and yelled there.

"These are worse," he thought, "than the Pamunkey war whoops on the banks of the Chickahominy River."

Suddenly the mat curtains were lifted. A man, painted black, came stamping in. At first John Smith did not recognize the devilish figure as the old Chief, Powhatan. There followed some two hundred other Indians, all whooping and yelling as they danced round his mat.

"Now," Powhatan said when the dancing was over. "Now, you are our brother. You are now free. When you go back to James Town, you must send me two cannons for killing my enemies. You must send, also, a grindstone to sharpen the iron tools you have given me. I will give you land for your own. You shall now call me 'Father,' and one day, you shall be a weroance of our tribes."

"Come back soon, my brother," Pocahontas called out when the twelve Powhatan guides made ready to set forth with Captain John Smith.

"I will come back," the white Captain promised.

"Come back soon! Or I will come after you!" the girl shouted gaily as she waved good-by.

But her white brother did not come back soon. Neither were the two cannons and the grindstone brought back by the twelve Powhatans who had gone with him.

"The cannons were too heavy for us to carry, Wahunsonacock," the men excused themselves. "And we feared their magic." Then they told what had happened when they arrived at James Town.

"The Long Knives there received us as their friends. They rejoiced that their great weroance was safe and free. At his bidding, they brought two cannons out for us, and the grindstone.

"We asked that the cannons should be fired so that we could be sure that they were not broken. The giant thunder-tubes were loaded with stones and bits of metal. The Pale Faces turned the cannons' mouths toward the forest. Then they made them speak.

"You would have been frightened, too, Wahunsonacock, if you had heard the thunder of those cannons. You, too, would have run away when those icy branches fell crashing down on the ground."

Powhatan's face showed his disappointment. It did not brighten until the men laid before him the pile of other presents which the men of James Town had sent him in place of the cannons and the grindstone.

Blue Beads Save the Day

"WE bring gifts for my brother, Captain John Smith."

Pocahontas spoke shyly to the settlers who were gathered at the gate of the James Town Fort. Each of the young Indians behind her was carrying some kind of food. They had brought deer meat and turkeys, squirrels and fish, as well as baskets of corn.

Food was the chief riches of the people of America in those days. It was the best the Indians could offer to their pale-faced neighbors. And it was the gift that was most welcome to these hungry white men.

It was true that the ship of Captain Newport had returned, bringing provisions from over the sea. But that ship brought also many new settlers, and they, too, must be fed. There was not enough of anything at James Town to last very long.

On this day the eyes of the settlers were more often turned upon the Indian girl than upon the food she had brought. Everyone wanted to look at The Powhatan's daughter who had saved their leader, John Smith.

The Powhatan's daughter was gay, and pretty to look at. How she smiled when Captain John Smith came running to meet her! How fond she seemed to be of her "new brother"!

Everyone at James Town made much of their Indian visitors that day. They showed them their fort with its great cannon. They took them inside their strange square wooden houses.

Most exciting of all for the young Indians was their visit aboard the giant canoe which had brought Captain Newport back over the sea.

"There were beds in that great canoe," Pocahontas told The Powhatan. "The white Manitos could sleep comfortably each night during their long journey.

"The weroance, Captain Newport, is not so splendid to look at as our brother, Captain John Smith," she added. "Yet he is more powerful. John Smith calls him his 'Great Father.' He says all at James Town are the children of Newport. It is only when Newport is gone, that John Smith rules there."

Perhaps it was her love for Captain John Smith.

Blue Beads Save the Day

Or it may have been her curiosity about the white Manitos. Whatever the reason, Pocahontas persuaded her father to send her with food for the settlers every few days.

It was not far to James Town from Werowocomico. Pocahontas and her little band could make the journey there through the forest and over the river in less than half a day. With each visit, the Indian girl felt more at home. Soon she was talking and laughing merrily with her new friends among the Long Knives.

One day, Tom Savage, a settler boy her own age, was showing off before Pocahontas and her companions. He had learned to stand upside down on his hands with his heels in the air, and he was proud of this trick.

"Look!" he cried. "Look at me!"

But before he was right side up again, Pocahontas had thrown off her deerskin cloak. Her tawny body was almost bare, but she did not seem to mind the biting winter chill.

"Look!" she cried. "Look at me!" And she turned a splendid cartwheel. First one hand on the ground! Next the other hand! Then back on her feet again.

Upside down on her two hands, Pocahontas walked all around the amazed settler boy. Then she turned three more cartwheels in a row. Other laughing young Indians followed her lead. But Pocahontas was easily the best of them all.

In Werowocomico, after each journey, Pocahontas reported all the things she had seen. She told her father how the Pale Faces' village had burned to the ground. How the men, now, were beginning to build their houses again, and so they had no time either to hunt or to fish.

"Captain Newport's ship has brought many men. The other ships are bringing still more," she told her father. "They will need a great deal of corn."

Pocahontas was right. The settlers did need a great deal of corn. The two captains, with thirty strong men to guard them, rowed their barge down the Powhatan River and up the Pamunkey to Werowocomico. When Captain John Smith went ashore in the little canoe, there were shouts of welcome from the Indians watching for him on the river bank.

With Pocahontas at his side, and with two hundred Indian warriors coming behind, Captain John Smith and his guards were escorted to The Powhatan's wigwam.

Once again, the old Chief was dressed in his mantle of raccoon skins and tails. As before, he was seated on his bed-throne, with his young wives at his side and his warriors round the walls. But this time, his welcome was for a brother, not for a prisoner. There was a smile upon his stern face.

"Welcome, my son and my brother! Your visit makes my heart glad," the old Chief said to his guest.

Blue Beads Save the Day

"But where is your great weroance, Captain Newport?"

"My father, Newport, rests on our barge," the Captain replied. "I come ahead to prepare for his visit. When the sun rises again, my father Newport will come ashore to greet The Powhatan."

"Bid your men come before me." Powhatan was speaking now of Captain John Smith's guards, who stood just outside the door opening of his wigwam. "They shall have all the corn bread they can eat.

"First let them lay down their guns here at my feet. The Pale Faces and the Powhatans are brothers now. There is no need for your guns. See, my braves have laid down their arrows. Bid your men also lay down their long knives. I swear no harm shall come to them."

But Captain John Smith was wary. He had learned that even when the Indians called him their brother, they might be planning some trick.

"It is not our custom," John Smith replied to The Powhatan. "We do not lay down our arms. But have no fear. Our guns shall not harm our Indian brothers so long as there is peace between us."

And though twice again The Powhatan asked that the guns be put away, Captain John Smith refused.

Next morning, with a trumpeter marching ahead, and with guards of honor on each side, Captain John Smith led Captain Newport to Powhatan's wigwam.

Again the Queen of Appomatuck brought fresh water for washing the hands of the guests. Again soft turkey feathers were brought to dry them. And again a great feast was served.

"As long as the sun shines and the rivers run, there shall be friendship between us and our brothers from over the sea." So The Powhatan began his welcome to his guests.

It was a fine speech. In splendid words the old Indian told of his love for Captain John Smith and his new friend, Captain Newport.

"I make you a present, Great Weroance," The Powhatan said to Captain Newport. "My pale-faced brothers should learn more about our Powhatan ways. So I give you this young brave, Namontacke, to be your son. He shall dwell with you in James Town. He shall learn to speak your words. He shall teach you our ways."

John Smith suspected that the old Chief also was thinking that Namontacke, living at James Town, could easily keep him informed about the Pale Faces and their plans.

"In return, one of our brothers shall dwell in the wigwams of the Powhatans," Captain Newport replied. "We shall leave this bright lad with you. He, also, shall live with you as a son." It was Tom Savage, Pocahontas saw, the boy who had turned cart wheels with her on her first visit to James Town.

Blue Beads Save the Day

For three days there was feasting, singing, and dancing in honor of the two captains from James Town. Then the trading began.

It was Captain Newport who now spoke for the settlers. Perhaps he was jealous of the liking which the Powhatans showed for Captain John Smith. Perhaps he wanted too badly to be liked just as much. For it was soon clear to everyone that he was giving The Powhatan too much for too little.

"Our father is getting the best of this stranger," Pocahontas whispered to Nantakas. "Only four baskets does he give to Captain Newport for presents that are worth a whole barge full of corn."

Pocahontas could see that Captain John Smith also had noticed. She could see, too, that her father was growing more and more sure of his power over the new white weroance.

"Lay out your hatchets and your copper! Put down your long knives and your tools! I will choose what I like. Then I will pay what I like."

Captain John Smith looked with dismay at the few baskets of corn. Then he sent off a runner to the barge in the river.

"I have other treasures here to show to The Powhatan," he said when the runner returned. And he laid on the earth floor of the wigwam a basket of trinkets—bells made of brass and beads made of blue glass.

"Look!" Pocahontas cried in delight. "Here are beads of the color of the blue sky itself. Never before have I seen blue beads like these."

"I will have the blue beads," Powhatan said, scooping a handful up out of the basket. "I will give you ten baskets of corn for these blue beads."

Captain John Smith saw the pleasure in the dark eyes of the old Chief. It did not matter that these blue beads were of the cheapest of glass. Here was something The Powhatan truly wanted to own.

So John Smith shook his head.

"I could not sell you the blue beads, Wahunsonacock," he said. "Beads the color of the heavens are beyond reasonable price. It would take at least three hundred baskets of corn to pay for the blue beads here in my basket."

"I will have the sky-colored beads," Powhatan insisted.

"Only the greatest kings may wear beads of the color of Manito's heaven," John Smith declared.

"I am the mighty King of all the Powhatan tribes. I will have the blue beads," The Powhatan cried again. "I will pay what you ask but I will have the blue beads."

So it was that Captain John Smith and his blue beads saved the day for the white traders. Baskets and baskets of corn were loaded into his barge. They made up for the few which Newport had bought so dearly.

Blue Beads Save the Day

And before he went away, Captain John Smith said with a smile, "Bid Pocahontas to bring me a little basket. I will fill it with blue beads as a present for my dear sister." He was proud that he could say this in Indian words.

The Powhatan was greatly pleased with his bargain. He gave orders that no one in his Powhatan empire, except weroances and their families, might wear the royal blue beads.

"Dear and Blessed Pocahontas"

"They are loading Newport's giant canoe. Soon, very soon, Wahunsonacock, that weroance will go back to his country over the sea."

It was Namontacke speaking, the one whom the old Indian Chief had given into the service of the white leader. From time to time, in secret, the young Indian made his way back to Werowocomico to report to The Powhatan.

"They are loading the furs and the skins they have got from us in trade. They are laying in the boards they have cut from the cedars and walnut trees. But mostly, Great Weroance, they are filling their boat up with the yellow dirt they love so well."

The Indians listening in Powhatan's wigwam shook their heads. Truly, these pale-faced men often were stupid. Often they lost their way in the forest. They made their campfires with damp wood which would not burn well. They hung their cooking pots over new fires which still sent up clouds of black smoke.

And now, they thought they had found gold in that little stream beyond their village of James Town!

"How should the yellow bits in that stream be gold?" Namontacke was scornful. "Pound them and at once they become dust. They do not hold together under the pounding tool like true gold or copper. Their shining dust is only good for sprinkling over our body paint."

The Indians knew that this yellow dust was something quite different from gold. Today some people call it iron pyrites.

On the bed and in the banks of the stream, the yellow sands shone. They were bright, like the golden rings on the fingers of the white strangers. Men of many countries have been fooled by the glitter of iron pyrites. That is why this metal has often been known as "fool's gold."

"Captain John Smith tells the others that the yellow dirt is not gold. But they will not listen," Namontacke told The Powhatan. "They dig it out of the stream banks. They wash it and wash it to take the brown dirt away. And they load the shining yellow sand into their canoes with wings.

"The men of James Town do not take the time now

to hunt or to fish. They do not worry about planting their corn, although the time for planting is here. All they think of is this yellow sand."

"We should send presents to our brother, Captain Newport, before he goes away," Powhatan said when the young man had finished his tale of the "fool's gold." And the next day there stood at the gate of the James Town Fort a small band of Powhatans bearing twenty wild turkeys.

"This is a gift from The Powhatan for the weroance, Newport! The Powhatan asks, in return, a gift of twenty long knives." This was the message which those Indians brought.

"Twenty swords are too many for just twenty turkeys," Captain John Smith warned his leader. But Captain Newport would not listen. He still badly wanted to gain Powhatan's favor.

"I will give the twenty swords to The Powhatan," Captain Newport replied. And the messengers departed with the precious "long knives."

A short time after Captain Newport had sailed away, another ship from England arrived at the James Town landing. Word quickly spread all along the rivers, that this ship had brought a fine cargo of muskets and pistols, and sharp, shining swords.

Almost at once, runners from Werowocomico again stood at the gate of the James Town Fort.

"Dear and Blessed Pocahontas"

"The Powhatan now sends twenty turkeys for his brother, Captain John Smith," the Indians said. "From him, also, our weroance asks twenty long knives in return."

But Captain John Smith was wiser than Captain Newport. He knew well that the swords would be used by the Indians against himself and the other settlers. So the messengers from Powhatan were sent away with only their turkeys to take back home again.

"The weapons of the Pale Faces are far better than ours," Powhatan, disappointed, said to his men. "We cannot win battles with them unless we, too, have the guns that spit fire, and the sharp knives that cut at the lightest touch. Somehow, we must get more of these white men's tools of war.

"Borrow them! Steal them! Take them by force! But get me the weapons of the white men!" The Powhatan's voice was hard and determined when he gave the order.

The early times of peace between the Powhatans and the settlers seemed to be over. Now each feared the other. Each was on guard against a surprise attack.

Indians fell upon the settlers when they were rebuilding their church or at work in their corn fields. The Englishmen dared not go far into the forest, lest arrows should fly at them from behind the trunks of the trees. So bold did the Powhatan braves become that they even attacked the great Captain John Smith.

"Captain John Smith does not know fear." Namontacke told the story in his chief's wigwam. "Like a young deer, he led the chase after his Indian foes. All over the land he hunted them down.

"And when he caught them, he whipped them until they could not stand up."

Some of the settlers thought Captain John Smith was too cruel in his dealings with unfriendly Indians. All remembered that their English King had commanded that they treat these "red men" with kindness.

But Pocahontas did not think her white brother had done anything wrong. He had only acted as a brave weroance should. After all, he had been attacked by those whom he punished.

"What happened then, Namontacke?" the girl cried from her seat beside her old father.

"Seven of our strongest and bravest young Powhatans were captured by the white weroance. He holds them prisoner inside the James Town fort."

Namontacke had listened well to the talk in the square houses of James Town. It was he who told The Powhatan and Pocahontas how it all happened there.

"Captain John Smith chose one from among his seven Indian prisoners. 'This one shall go with my men into the deep woods,' the white weroance told the

"*Get me the weapons of the white men,*" Powhatan commanded his warriors.

"Dear and Blessed Pocahontas"

others. 'Listen well! The voice of a gun will tell you what happens to him there.'

"The six prisoners listened in silence. Then they heard the terrible voice of the thunder-tube. Then they were sure their companion was dead.

" 'Will you follow your brother into the woods?' Captain John Smith asked them in a threatening voice. 'Or will you speak truly and tell me why the Powhatans make war upon their peaceful white brothers?'

"The six chose to speak, Wahunsonacock. They told how you, our Great Father, had commanded them to bring back the guns and the long knives. They told how they were to use the swords, which they took from the Pale Faces, to cut their white throats.

"In return, the white weroance did not harm the six prisoners." These words were welcome to those who were listening. "In truth, the Captain had not harmed that one whom he sent off into the forest. The sound of the shot was only a trick to make the other six speak."

"My white brother is kind." Pocahontas spoke eagerly.

"When will he set the prisoners free?" Powhatan demanded.

"He does not say, Great Weroance, what he will do with them."

Powhatan's face was dark. These seven prisoners were among the best of his warriors. They were dear to the tribe. Somehow, they must be saved.

Then his face brightened.

"We shall send Pocahontas to free them," he cried. "Pocahontas shall ask for their lives from her white brother who loves her so dearly."

A young girl, scarcely more than thirteen years old, was a strange one to make peace between a powerful weroance and a great English captain. But Pocahontas went gladly. Bravely, she led the way for the band of Powhatans whom her father sent to accompany her.

"My father sends presents to his adopted son," the little Indian girl said to Captain John Smith. "The Powhatan begs you to excuse his foolish men. He did not really mean them to harm his Pale Face friends. Let the seven prisoners go free, my brother! And, forever, you shall have The Powhatan's love."

Captain John Smith looked tenderly at the eager face of the Indian girl. Here was one Powhatan who never wavered in her friendship for him and his people.

"For my dear and blessed Pocahontas, it shall be done," he said, smiling down at her. And he gave the seven prisoners over into her keeping.

"Dear and blessed Pocahontas," was the way in which many of the white settlers talked of this young peacemaker. They knew it was chiefly because of Pocahontas that the Indian attacks on their fort now were stopped, at least for a while.

A Dance for the Captain and a Crown for the King

Pocahontas was excited.
"He is coming to Werowocomico. My white brother is coming," she cried to the women in Powhatan's wigwam. "White Owl has brought the word. Captain John Smith and four others are even now crossing the river."

The girl had not seen her beloved white brother for many weeks. All through that summer of 1608, Captain John Smith and his men were sailing up and down the rivers of this part of America. The Captain was making a map of the four broad streams which could be entered from the Great Salt Water Bay. Up

A Dance for the Captain and a Crown for the King

the Powhatan and its branch, the Chickahominy, along the Pamunkey and the Tappahannock, even thirty miles up the Potomac River, they went.

The Powhatans' Corn Feast was already over when John Smith returned from his second long journey along the four rivers. Captain Newport's ship again had come back from over the sea. It had brought many new settlers, new supplies of food, tools, guns, and swords.

There was much work to do in the growing village of James Town. The new settlers were welcome. They could help build houses and make glass and soap ashes. For the first time, there were Pale Face women in the little town. Two had come over on Captain Newport's ship.

"I bring the greetings of our English King to The Powhatan," Captain John Smith said when he had landed at Werowocomico.

"You are welcome here, my father!" It was Pocahontas who greeted him. She liked to call Captain John Smith by this title, "Father," which her people gave to those they most loved and respected.

"The Powhatan is away. He did not know that his brother, Captain John Smith, was coming to Werowocomico."

"I bring a message from Captain Newport," John Smith explained. "In his ship, he has brought presents for The Powhatan. Our good King James has sent

The Powhatan a shining gilt crown, a crown such as great kings wear in our world over the sea. He has sent him a rich red royal robe, and a great bed such as we sleep in. There are other gifts, too."

"We will send a runner at once." Pocahontas was impressed. "The Powhatan is only one sleep away, just up the river. I will make a feast for our visitors until he can return."

A fire was built in a meadow on the edge of the woods. Reed mats were spread near it for Captain John Smith and the four companions who had come with him. The afternoon was cool, and the warmth of the blazing fire was welcome. The fragrance of its burning made the air sweet and spicy.

It was pleasant to rest there. The Time of Falling Leaves was near. Already the woods were bright with the reds of the maples. The oaks and the walnut trees and the tulip poplars were turning yellow and brown. And the afternoon sky was clear and blue overhead.

"Wait here a little, my father," Pocahontas said to her guest. "Wait and I shall have a fine surprise for you."

While they waited, the Englishmen talked together about the cargo which Captain Newport had brought over the sea. They talked, also, of the messages he had brought from their King.

A Dance for the Captain and a Crown for the King

The crowd of Indians who stood watching them could not understand much of what they said. But they could see that their white visitors were not happy or smiling.

"Our King demands gold, and there is no gold here." John Smith was speaking. "He demands a way to the western sea, but mountains stand in the way. And now he thinks that he can buy peace with The Powhatan for a gilt crown and a red robe, a bed and a pitcher."

So the settlers were talking among themselves when a great noise burst upon their ears. Surely it came from the nearby woods. There was yelling and howling. It was as if a pack of wolves or a band of enemy Indians was about to attack them.

"A trick!" cried one settler. "The Powhatans surround us!"

Captain John Smith jumped to his feet. He grabbed up his gun from beside him on the reed mat. And he took firm hold of two of the Indians in the crowd nearby. He was ready to use them as a shield against arrows which might come flying out of the woods.

The crowd of watching Indians laughed. They laughed and laughed at the startled Englishmen. For it was only Pocahontas who came dancing out of the forest with a band of her friends.

The girl's body was painted red with puccoon powder and bear grease. Her only garments were two otter skins and an apron of bright green leaves. On her head she had tied a pair of branching deer antlers. A quiver of arrows hung at her side, and her bow was bent back as she danced up to her guests.

"Have no fear, my dear father," she cried when she saw that the din had brought Captain John Smith to his feet. "There is no harm intended. You shall have my life if I do not tell you the truth. This is a dance for you, my father. It is to give you pleasure. Pray sit down on your mat again."

Thirty Powhatan girls and young women had followed Pocahontas out of the woods. Each one was dressed in an apron made of green leaves. And each had deer antlers upon her head.

O, they were a merry band. Their long black hair streamed about their painted bodies. Some were painted bright red. Others were painted black or white. Still others had several colors in the patterns they had put upon their tawny skins.

As they capered before the reed mats of their visitors, the slender brown legs of the Indian girls flashed in the sun. They sang and they danced and they leaped about upon the green meadow.

When the dancing was over, each girl picked up a burning stick from the fire. These lighted their way through the evening dusk to the wigwam where the visitors were to sleep.

"We love you, our Pale Face brothers. O, do you

A Dance for the Captain and a Crown for the King

not love us?" the merry girls cried over and over, as they followed the Englishmen into the wigwam.

The embarrassed settlers were glad when the older women began to bring in the platters of deer meat for the feast. They were glad, also, when his log canoe brought the Powhatan back to Werowocomico the next day.

"Captain Newport invites the Powhatan to come to James Town to receive the gifts which our King has sent from over the sea. The Powhatan is to be crowned by the order of King James." So Captain John Smith delivered his message.

"My heart is glad that your King has sent presents," The Powhatan replied. There was a puzzled look in his keen eyes. "But I shall not go to James Town. King James is king in his land. I am king in my land. In this Powhatan country, all people must come to The Powhatan.

"Presents can be good bait for a trap," The Powhatan continued. "I will not set foot inside your English fort. But I will wait eight days here at Werowocomico. Captain Newport can bring your King's gifts to me here." It was very plain that the old Chief did not trust his white brothers.

So Captain Newport sent the King's presents for Powhatan to Werowocomico. The sailing barge brought them on the hundred-mile journey down the Powhatan River and up the Pamunkey.

That was a strange coronation, the crowning of Powhatan. Neither he nor his people quite knew what to make of the doings of their white brothers that day.

They watched with wide eyes the gifts that were unloaded from the Englishmen's barge. The gilt crown shone in the sunshine. The red of the royal mantle was the color of blood.

Captain John Smith showed them the use of the shining brass pitcher and basin. He said they were for washing The Powhatan's hands.

Before the curious eyes of the Indians, a carpenter put together the great wooden bed which stood so high off the ground. The Powhatans felt of the stuffed mattress and the soft pillows. They looked at each other with questions in their minds. Could it be that this was some trap that would do harm to their Weroance? Then they laughed when one Pale Face lay down upon it to show that it was for sleeping.

Next, Captain Newport was holding the golden crown out in his two hands.

"Now we do honor to the King of the Powhatans. To be crowned in our fashion, he must kneel at my feet," he said to the watching crowd.

"The Powhatan kneels at no man's feet." The old Chief's eyes were flashing with indignation. He did not like this "honor."

A Dance for the Captain and a Crown for the King

"I cannot place the crown properly unless you bend down. You are too tall." Captain Newport was growing angry.

But The Powhatan would not stoop. Tall and proud, he stood still. And his face was grim.

"They mean no harm," said Namontacke, who had made the journey to England with Newport. But The Powhatan would not bend his head.

Pocahontas trusted her friend, Captain John Smith. But, like the other Indians watching, she was troubled when Captain Newport pressed with all his might on the shoulders of the King of the Powhatans. What kind of treatment was this for such a great weroance?

Somehow, Captain Newport succeeded in pushing Powhatan into a position where he could place the gilded crown upon his gray head. Captain John Smith then threw the royal red mantle over the Chief's bare shoulders. All the Englishmen drew sighs of relief that the Indian King at last had been crowned as it had been ordered in England.

As soon as the strange coronation was over, one of the English guards at the wigwam door fired a shot from his pistol into the air. The newly crowned King jumped with surprise at the sound.

Answering thunder came from the cannon on the settlers' barge at the landing. And the startled

Powhatan ran out of the wigwam to hide in the woods. His crown slipped to one side, and his royal robe streamed out behind him. He ran like the wind.

The Englishmen watching could not help smiling.

"It was only a kingly salute in your honor, Wahunsonacock," Captain John Smith explained when he found the Great Weroance behind a huge oak tree. "Shooting our cannon is our way of telling the world of the crowning of a great king."

When the beating of his old heart had become calmer, The Powhatan spoke with great dignity.

"I thank my brother, King James, for the gifts he has sent me, and I send him gifts in return. I send him my fur mantle for the royal red robe. And I send him my own moccasins to ease his feet."

Powhatan kicked off his old deerskin shoes. And he handed his worn mantle of raccoon skins to the astonished Captain Newport.

"You shall have also a present of eight baskets of corn for the bed and the crown and the pitcher and basin," Powhatan added.

Captain John Smith muttered to one of the English guards who stood near. "What kind of an exchange of gifts is this? The Powhatan is not impressed with this play. I told Newport the whole business was a mistake. We could have had more corn for a hatchet and a few pieces of copper. Now, we shall have to pay dearly for the corn we must have to fill up our barge."

A Dance for the Captain and a Crown for the King

Through all the ceremonies and the trading, The Powhatan was polite to his visitors. Captain John Smith and Captain Newport were polite, too. But in spite of their friendly words, both Indians and Englishmen were ever watchful. Neither trusted the other. Both were glad when the barge took the white men down the river again.

A Messenger in the Dark

Pocahontas brushed the tears out of her eyes with the back of her hand. She did not want her father to ask her why she was crying.

With the women of Powhatan's wigwam, she was taking away the platters of food, left from the evening meal. And she could not help hearing the talk of the men, sitting about the fire hole.

"Starve the Long Knives!"

The Powhatan said it again. And his voice was hard.

"Hide the corn away in the forest! The Pale Faces need food. Without corn, these strangers will have to go away from our land."

"And what if their bold weroance will not let his children go away from this land?" Thunder Eagle was

A Messenger in the Dark

thinking of how Captain John Smith had turned his cannon upon his own homesick men when they had tried to sail away.

"We shall kill the white weroance. We shall set a trap for the bold Captain from which he cannot escape."

It was not surprising that Pocahontas wept when she heard her father speak these dreadful words.

What had come over The Powhatan? Why had he changed? He had adopted her white brother into the tribe. Her father had allowed her to take food again and again to the hungry men of James Town. And now, he spoke as if the Pale Faces were his most hated enemies.

"The Pale Faces are no friends of the Powhatans," the old Chief said. It was as if her father knew just what Pocahontas was thinking.

"They come here to trade, but they will stay to take our country away from us. Always new people come. None go away. Already, their ships have brought women. Soon, whole families will settle here. Soon, there will be no room for our own people in our own land."

Powhatan's command, "Starve the Long Knives!" went up and down all the rivers.

The Powhatan spoke truly when he said there was not enough to eat in the settlement at James Town. So hungry were the settlers that some foolish ones even traded their guns and their swords for a little corn or deer meat.

"Do not give weapons to the Indians!" Captain John Smith warned them again and again. "The Indians will shoot you with your own guns. They will use your own swords to cut your throats."

But many of those settlers did not listen. Many blamed John Smith, now their president, for their miserable lives. They thought he was too stern. They said he made them work too hard at cutting out house boards in the forest, and in preparing tar and soap ashes to send over the sea.

Like The Powhatan, a few unhappy settlers even plotted to kill their wise president. Again and again, while the geese were flying north that year, both Indians and settlers made such wicked plans. But, always, their plans failed. The bold, clever Captain was always on guard.

Then, one day, this invitation came from The Powhatan: "Let your house builders make for me a board house like those of James Town, Captain John Smith! Give me a grindstone with which to sharpen my tools! Send me fifty swords, a rooster and a hen, some copper and beads! And I will fill your barges with corn."

"Do not go to Werowocomico!" his friends warned John Smith. "It is surely a trap." But the Captain shook his head.

A Messenger in the Dark

"We must have the corn. I am not afraid. Who of you will go with me?"

Five house builders—two Englishmen and three Germans who had come on Newport's last voyage—were sent over the land to Werowocomico. Captain John Smith himself set forth with a small sailing ship and two barges and forty-six men.

It was the Time of Great Cold. The weather was bitter. Winter winds blew. Frost and snow dusted the land over with white. Ice covered the small streams and the edges of the rivers.

The party reached a landing place near Werowocomico on January 12th in this year of 1609. They found the Pamunkey River frozen far out from the land. And the ice had to be broken to bring a barge near enough for wading ashore.

Through icy water up to their waists, the men reached the land. They were wet to their skins. Their teeth chattered like one of Thunder Eagle's gourd rattles. They were glad to take shelter in the wigwams of the outpost on the edge of the river.

"Tell your Great Father, The Powhatan, we have come for the corn. And say we are hungry," John Smith told the Indian scouts there on the river bank.

It was not long before the runners returned with corn bread and turkey, fish and deer meat for their supper. When morning came, The Powhatan received them in his own wigwam, and more food was served.

But his greeting when they had eaten was a surprise.

"Why have you come here, Captain John Smith?" he asked. "Why don't you go away?" his voice was unfriendly.

"But you yourself invited us to come for the corn. Is your memory so short, then, Wahunsonacock?" The Captain was bewildered. "My men are already building you the house which you asked for. Did you not promise to fill my barges with corn, in return for the grindstone, the hen and the rooster, the beads and the copper which we have brought?"

Powhatan only laughed at his white visitor.

"How should I give you corn, my brother? We have not enough for our own cooking pots. And we cannot eat beads or copper!" The old Chief was scornful.

"Yet, I will look at the things you have brought," he continued. "If you have enough guns and long knives to trade, perhaps we can find the corn."

"I know well, O Powhatan, that you have hidden the corn. I know you have forbidden your people to share their food with us. I have no guns and no swords to spare. And I must have corn!" Captain John Smith tried not to show how angry he was. "I would be your friend, Weroance-of-All-Weroances," the white man

A Messenger in the Dark

continued patiently. "Only your own unkind treatment could spoil my love for my Powhatan brothers. My people are hungry. We must have corn."

"You shall have corn." The Powhatan also hid his true feelings, now, under soft words. "But if you are truly my brother, why do you not leave your guns and your long knives outside my wigwam?"

"That is not our custom. I have said it before." Captain John Smith was firm. "Our guns and our swords are as much a part of our clothing as our jackets and cloaks. We do not put them aside." He knew well that The Powhatan was only waiting for a chance to catch him unarmed.

The talk went on politely. And, at last, they did trade. The amount of corn was agreed on and, outside, the Indians began to cut a way through the ice. Then the barges could be brought near enough to be loaded with the corn.

Suddenly Captain John Smith noticed that The Powhatan had slipped out of the wigwam. Most of his wives and all of the children also were gone. Only two women remained there to entertain the visitors.

Before the Englishmen could ask a question, there was a rush of moccasined feet. There was the hard breathing of running men. Indians filled the great wigwam. Their spears and tomahawks were held ready to strike.

But John Smith was ready. A shot rang from his gun, and the Indians turned tail. Their brown bodies tumbled over each other in their hurry to get away through the door of Powhatan's house.

Captain John Smith and his angry companions made their way safely to the wigwams of the outposts on the river bank. Hardly had they arrived, than they had an Indian visitor. This man was old, so old it was plain he could not harm them. And he brought them a message.

"The Powhatan meant no harm. He went away only because he was afraid of his white brothers' guns," the old Indian declared.

"The ice is open now. And The Powhatan begs his white brothers to take their corn and go away. He sends these presents to show that he still is their friend." The old man put into Smith's hands a broad armlet and a very fine necklace made of white shell beads.

With frequent looks at the guns of the Englishmen, the Indians loaded the corn into the barges. With baskets on their strong backs, they trotted down to the landing. The barges were filled well before the winter night spread its black blanket over the land.

"We shall have to wait for high water," Captain John Smith said, after one look at the river.

A Messenger in the Dark

The ocean tides sweep in and out of all the streams that empty into Chesapeake Bay. Boatmen there have to reckon with high tides and low tides.

Leaving a party to guard the corn on the barges, John Smith and the other settlers went into the outpost wigwam to keep warm.

The Indians had disappeared. The winter sky now was covered with clouds. It was so black outside that one scarcely could see the outline of the barges.

The settlers, sitting about the fire in the wigwam, started up when they heard the door mat put aside. They could scarcely believe their own eyes. Standing there in the doorway was the slender figure of The Powhatan's daughter.

The girl was panting with running. There were tears on her cheeks. And she sobbed as she spoke to Captain John Smith.

"Go quickly, my brother! Go away now! My father, The Powhatan, means to kill you this night.

"He is sending you food. His men are even now close behind me on the forest path. But they do not bring the feast just for your pleasure. While you are eating, they mean to seize your guns and your swords. If the braves do not kill you, The Powhatan himself will come this night to see that the deed is done. Go! O, go quickly!"

Captain John Smith put his arm around the shoulder of the trembling Pocahontas. It must have been a frightening journey on so black a night for so small a girl. He smoothed her black hair which was tangled with twigs that had been caught in it as she ran through the woods.

"My little sister! My dearest friend!" he cried, fondly. "How can I reward you? What gift will you have from us?" He would have given her anything she desired.

"I can take nothing! Nothing! No, I dare not," Pocahontas said, with tears of excitement still rolling down her cheeks. "If he found out about this night, my father would kill me, even me, his dear daughter." And pressing the hand of her beloved friend, Pocahontas ran out again into the darkness.

Hardly was she gone than ten tall Indian braves brought in a feast, just as she had said they would. John Smith made them taste each platter of turkey and each roast of deer meat. Only in this way could he be sure that the food had not been poisoned by The Powhatan.

"We shall eat now," he then said to the Indians. "Go back to The Powhatan. Give him our thanks for the food. Tell him, if he comes to see me this night, I shall be ready. I shall be watching for him."

Other Indians and still others came to that outpost wigwam on the river. And to each band Captain John Smith gave the same word, "I am ready to receive The Powhatan."

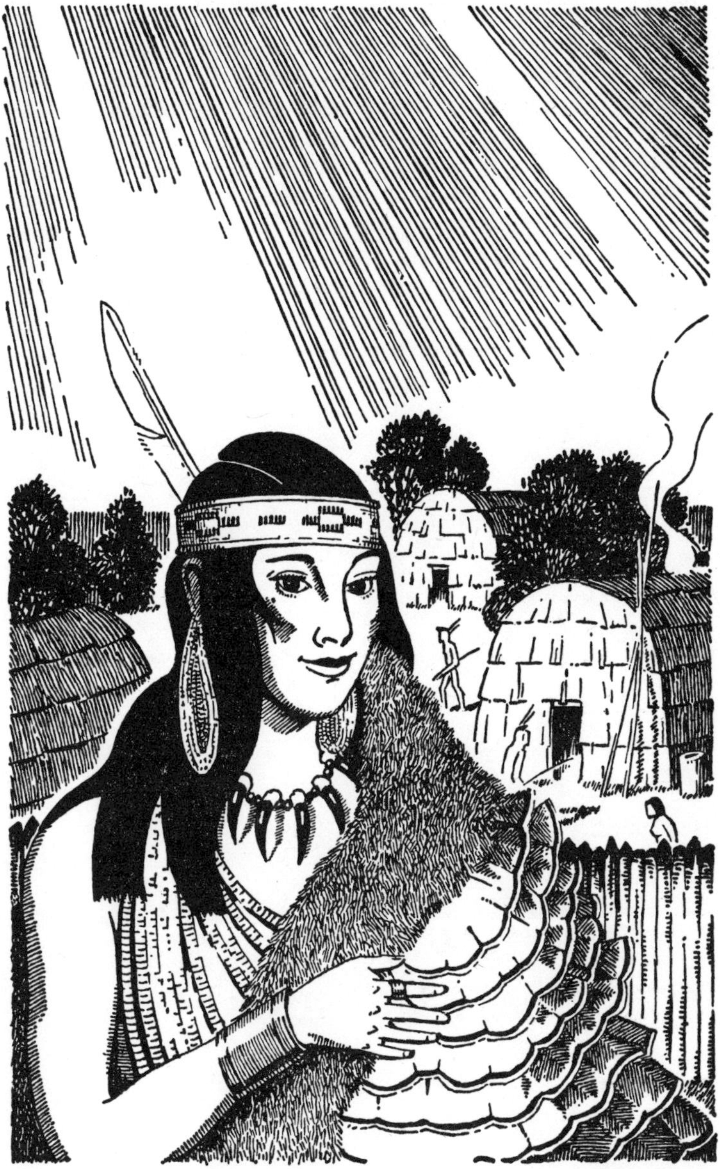

A Messenger in the Dark

"*Ai*, the white man is a wizard. He knows what is planned. His men have their guns always in their hands. There is no chance of surprising them." Each band of messengers made the same report to The Powhatan. So the plot failed.

When the water was high enough, the ship and the barges took Captain John Smith and his men away down the river. Each one of the settlers felt safer when he could no longer see the Werowocomico landing. As he thought of the night which was just past, each one of that party must have murmured to himself, "The dear and blessed Pocahontas! She has saved our lives once again."

Captain John Smith Sails Away

STRANGE stories about Captain John Smith were being told in the wigwams. Each tale was more amazing than the last. But everybody was sure the stories were true. People had seen his miracles happen with their own eyes.

"The white wizard's magic is mighty," the Indians said again and again. "Manito walks at his side."

There was the story of the three young Chickahominy braves who stole the pistol at James Town. The one who carried off the pistol got away safely into the forest. But the others—the two brothers who helped him—they were caught by Captain John Smith and his men.

Captain John Smith Sails Away

"This one shall be our prisoner," the Captain pointed to one of the brothers.

"And you," he said to the other. "You shall go after the thief and bring back my pistol. If you do not have it here before the sun rises again, your brother shall die."

Swiftly, like a young rabbit, the Indian youth ran

FROM *The Indian Races of North America*
by Charles De Wolf Brownell

Captain John Smith.

off into the forest. And his brother was locked up in the prison of the James Town Fort.

Captain John Smith felt sorry for the young Indian in his cold prison hut. He sent him water and food. And he gave him charcoal for a fire to keep himself warm during the chilly night.

Out of breath with hard running, the prisoner's brother came back in time. And when the pistol had been given to Captain John Smith, they went out together to set the prisoner free.

When they opened the prison hut, a cloud of black smoke rolled up into their faces. It made their eyes smart so that at first they could not see the Indian youth. And he did not answer their calls.

When the smoke cleared away, they found him lying there on the ground, as still as if he were dead. The black smoke from the charcoal fire had smothered him. He had fainted away. He did not even seem to feel the burning of the hot embers upon which he had fallen.

"*Ai-i-i-i-i! Ai-l-i-i-i!* My brother is dead," the young runner cried out. His piteous wails could be heard in all the houses of James Town.

But when Captain John Smith bent over the prisoner, he saw that there was still breath in his body. The Englishman straightened up. And he spoke kindly to the wailing brother. "Promise you will not steal from us again, and I will bring your brother back to life."

Whiskey and vinegar were poured in between the prisoner's lips. John Smith rubbed his limp body. Suddenly the young Indian opened his eyes. The settlers treated his burns, and they gave him a comfortable bed near a warm fire.

"With my own eyes, I saw the miracle happen. I saw the white wizard bring back my brother from Manito's land." So the young Indian told it when the two were again at home in their own village.

The Powhatans were telling, also, the story of how the bold English Captain, with only fifteen companions, escaped from an army of Pamunkey warriors.

The settlers had landed their barge near the town of Pamunkey, and Opekankano, the weroance, had welcomed them there with a feast. They ate at his fireside for many days. Then their trading began.

Opekankano had promised them corn. And they had brought copper, beads, and sharp tools with which to pay for it.

The two chiefs, the white chief and the Indian chief, sat facing each other in Opekankano's wigwam. Suddenly their talk was interrupted. One of Captain John Smith's men ran in through the door opening.

"Seven hundred Pamunkeys have surrounded this

place," the runner cried out. "Their bows and their arrows are in their hands. Some have swords, as well." The man spoke quickly and in English, but it was plain that Opekankano guessed what he was saying.

"My men have brought the corn," the Pamunkey chief said at once. "They are here to protect it. If my Pale Face friend will but step outside, he will see what splendid corn I have brought for him."

But Captain John Smith was not so easily trapped. He looked up into the frightened face of his runner.

What could only sixteen Englishmen do against seven hundred Indian warriors? Captain John Smith thought swiftly.

With a leap to his feet, he seized the Indian chief by his long scalp lock of black hair. Holding the surprised Opekankano with a tight grip, he pushed him before him out of the wigwam door. The trembling Pamunkey weroance was half dead with fear when he felt the Englishman's pistol pressed against his side.

"Listen to me, Pamunkeys!" the bold Captain shouted so that all could hear. "Let an arrow or a sword shed but one drop of English blood, and I will shoot your king."

His words scarcely were needed to strike fear into the hearts of the amazed Pamunkeys. They were dumb at the sight of their great king being held by his scalp lock, with a pistol pointed at his breast. Who would have thought that any man on earth would dare

Captain John Smith Sails Away

to handle their great weroance in such a rough way?

"This time, I am not caught in the marsh." Captain John Smith was triumphant. "This time not I, but Opekankano is the prisoner. Only when my ship is loaded with the corn he has promised us, shall he go free.

"I know well you want to kill me, Pamunkeys. Well, here I stand! Shoot if you dare! But if, instead, you would be my friends, I will not harm your king. Nor any one of you. There can be peace between us."

Arrows and swords were all put out of sight then. Presents were brought. All the Pamunkeys declared they wished peace.

Stories like these frightened the Indians along the Powhatan and the Pamunkey and the Chickahominy rivers. They sent presents asking for peace. Guns, swords, and other treasures were brought back to James Town before the settlers knew they had been stolen. The thieves were sent to Captain John Smith for punishment. And for weeks, there was peace.

And then came a story which was harder to believe than all the others. It was told by Indian runners who sped swiftly over the land. It was passed from one canoe to the other at the river landings. Like a fire in the forest, the news spread through the villages.

"Captain John Smith is dying! From gunpowder burns, he lies at death's door!"

"I will not believe it. My white brother cannot die. Manito will not let him die!" Pocahontas cried when she heard the tale.

It had happened like this, so the story ran:

The Captain was on his way down the river from his new town of Powhatan. The Indians all knew how he had bought the land and the houses and the Indian fort there from their king. The price Captain John Smith had paid was a rich treasure of copper and his promise to help The Powhatan in his war with the neighboring Monacan tribe.

It was while Captain John Smith was asleep in his boat that the accident happened. Somehow a redhot ember fell into a bag of gunpowder beside him. With the sharp noise of thunder, the bag burst into flame.

The noise and a burning pain woke the Captain. His clothes were on fire. He was a living torch when he leaped over the side of the barge into the water.

The river put out the fire, but John Smith, weak with pain, was caught up in its swirling waters. He was near to drowning when his men pulled him back onto the barge.

Great burns seared his body. His companions thought he would die before the barge could make the long journey back to James Town.

"My white brother will not die," Pocahontas said it again and again. "Surely his own magic can save him. Why should he not work a miracle for himself,

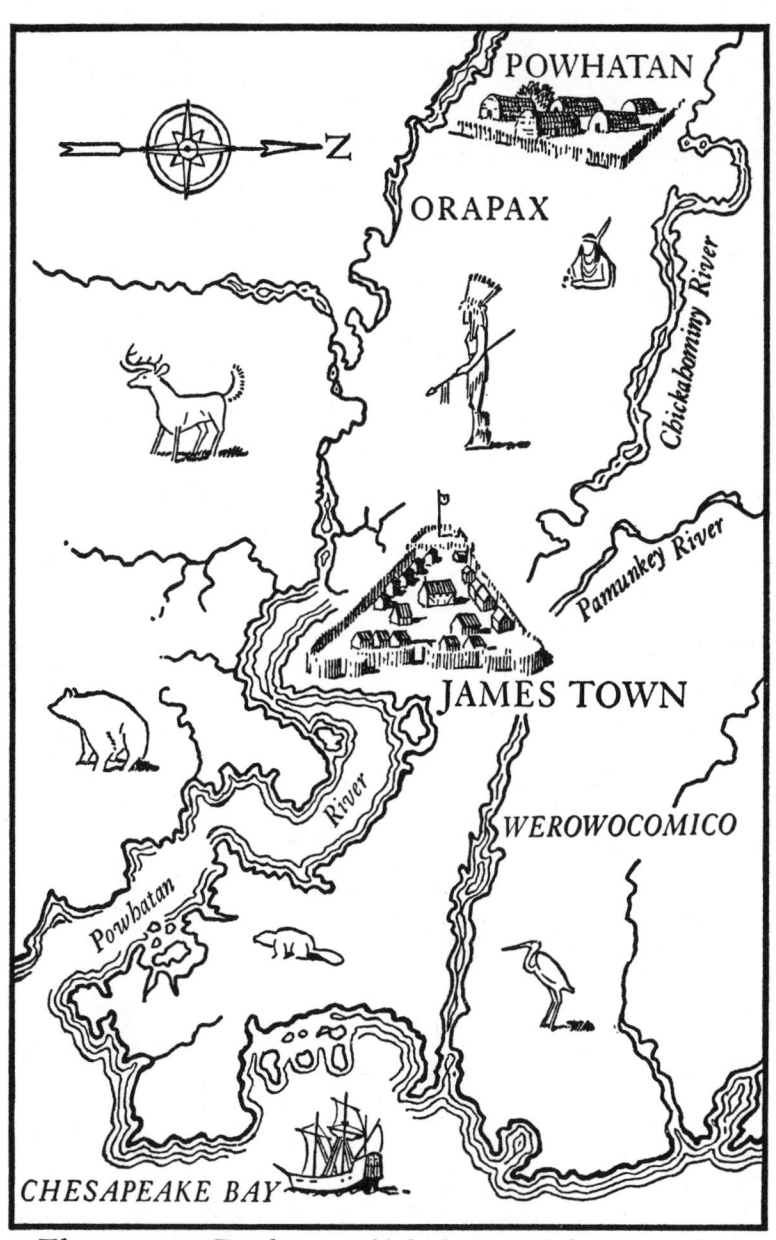

The town of Powhatan which Captain John Smith had bought was far up the river from James Town.

Captain John Smith Sails Away

just as he did for the pistol thief?" There were tears in her eyes, and she trembled with fear for her beloved friend.

The Indian girl would have run through the forest to James Town to see for herself how it was with Captain John Smith. But it was different there now.

Many, many new people—more than three hundred—had come with the last ships. All these newcomers, all these men, women, and children whom she did not know, were in James Town now.

Some even said there was to be a new governor in the Pale Face settlements. Captain John Smith no longer was to be its president. How this could be, none could understand, except perhaps Smith's English enemies who had plotted against him.

The new governor, Lord De La Warr, had not yet arrived. It was said that his ship had been blown away from the others in the midst of a tempest. But it might come any day.

Pocahontas herself, now, was no longer a child. She was fourteen years old. Now, she wore always the short fringed deerskin skirt of a grown girl. Almost, she was of an age to be married. She could not run about so freely as she had two years ago.

"Even though there are strangers in James Town, I will go there. I must find out the truth about my white brother," she said one day at last.

But before she could set out, news came that the dying Captain had sailed away. In the giant canoe with wings, he had gone home to die.

Many of the Indians rejoiced, but others were sorry to see him go away. "The white Captain was a brave man," they said. "He was bold in battle. He was fair in trade. He knew our ways. Truly, he was our friend."

They spoke as if Captain John Smith were already dead. For many nights, lying on her low bed in Powhatan's wigwam, Pocahontas cried herself to sleep.

A Princess Is Kidnapped

An English captain and his Indian friend were talking on the banks of the Potomac River.

This captain's name was Samuel Argall. He was the same Captain Argall who had sailed the giant canoes back and forth across the wide waters between England and its new colony in America. He also sailed smaller ships on trading journeys up and down the rivers of this land, which his people called Virginia.

The Indian's name was Japazaws, and he was the weroance of the Potomac tribes. Captain John Smith had made this Japazaws his friend. Captain Argall had adopted him as a brother. Japazaws was a weroance on whom the settlers could always count for friendship and trade.

"We need your help, Japazaws," Captain Argall

said that day to his Indian friend. "The warfare between the Powhatans and our people must come to an end. The bad times are behind us now. Our new governor rules well. But we must have peace with our Indian brothers."

When his visitor spoke of the "bad times" of the past, Japazaws shook his head with understanding. All the Virginia tribes knew how it had been in James Town after Captain John Smith went away. How the foolish settlers had wasted the stores he had left them! How they had not bothered to provide more food for the winter from the forest or fields!

Powhatan had rejoiced to see his Pale Face neighbors grow weak from want of food. Stories of their sicknesses made the old Chief's heart glad. During the "Starving Time," that terrible winter of 1610, settlers died every day from hunger, sickness, or cold.

The hungry Englishmen traded their swords, guns, and tools for such corn and deer meat as they could get from the Indians. They ate up their cows, their hogs, their sheep, and their goats. They even made soup of their horses' hides.

"It will be easy to crush the Pale Faces now that they are so weak and so sick," The Powhatan said to his warriors.

So many died that at last only sixty were left of the five hundred people to whom Captain John Smith had said, "Good-by." These were so weak that they could not cut firewood in the forest. Instead, they burned the palings of their fort, and the boards from their houses.

"Soon, the Long Knives will have to go away! Our land will be our own again!" These words of The Powhatan seemed to be coming true now.

Powhatan would have been right, had it not been for the arrival of the settlement's new governor, Lord De La Warr. The settlers had decided to give up and go back to England for good. They had been so unhappy that they wanted to burn all the James Town houses down to the ground before they sailed away.

Fortunately, their leaders had not let them set their houses on fire. For Lord De La Warr, named by King James to rule over his little colony in Virginia, turned their ships back from Chesapeake Bay.

The governor's ships from over the sea were filled with good food. They brought guns, swords and tools, medicines and supplies. In them were all the things the settlers would need for many a month. Back again in their old houses, the people took heart. Now the settlement was given another chance to live and grow.

"It was unlucky that Lord De La Warr fell ill so soon and had to go back to England," Captain Argall said to Japazaws that day on the Potomac River. "But we have a good governor now in Sir Thomas Dale.

If it were not for our war with The Powhatan, all would be well.

"The Powhatan still tries to drive us away from this land," Captain Argall continued. "If only Captain John Smith were here to make peace with him! If only Pocahontas would help us to persuade the old Chief her father!

"Is Pocahontas still our friend? We have not seen her in James Town since Captain John Smith went away. What has become of The Powhatan's daughter?"

"The year after her 'white brother' went away, when she was fifteen years old, Pocahontas was married for a short time to an Indian brave whose name was Kocoum," Japazaws told his visitor. "I do not know if Kocoum was killed in a battle. I do not know what has happened to him. But Pocahontas is not married to him now. That I know surely, for she is here, alone, in our own wigwams."

"Here? With the Potomacs?" Captain Argall could scarcely believe this piece of good fortune.

"She came here with a trading party sent by The Powhatan," Japazaws replied. "For three months she has been our guest."

Captain Argall was thoughtful. First he thought, "If Pocahontas still loves us, perhaps she will help us." Then a bolder idea came to him.

"Bring The Powhatan's daughter onto my ship, good friend Japazaws!" he said softly. "Once Pocahontas

A Princess Is Kidnapped

is on my ship, we shall take her with us to James Town. We can keep her there as our guest, until The Powhatan makes peace to have her set free."

"O, I dare not do that. The Powhatan would be angry. He would make war on the Potomacs." There was fear in the voice of the Indian, Japazaws.

"We will protect you from the Powhatans," Captain Argall promised. "We will treat Pocahontas as if she were our own sister. And you shall have as reward a fine big copper kettle!" The Captain was sure this shining copper pot was a treasure which would greatly tempt the Indian chief.

So it was that the next day the weroance, Japazaws, his wife and their guest, The Powhatan's daughter, came down to the ship landing.

This was a different Pocahontas from the child Captain John Smith left behind him. She was now seventeen, as pretty an Indian girl as there was in the land. She carried her head high, as should the daughter of the great king of all the Powhatan tribes.

"Let us go on board the ship, Pocahontas!" The wife of Japazaws spoke the words her husband had taught her during the night. "I want to see the inside of this giant English canoe."

"I will remain on the river bank. I have seen many such canoes," Pocahontas replied. Her father was at war, now, with the Englishmen. Her dear Captain John

Smith was not there to protect her. She did not know this Captain Argall.

"I want to go aboard! I want to go aboard!" Japazaws' wife played her part well.

"Be quiet, woman," Japazaws scolded her. "Be quiet or I will beat you. You shall not go on board the canoe without Pocahontas."

The woman insisted with tears in her eyes. But her husband refused until at last the soft-hearted Pocahontas gave in and said she would go aboard with her.

A warm friendly welcome from Captain Argall made the girl's fears disappear. She was merry at the fine feast that was spread in her honor.

Pocahontas could not see that, under the table, Japazaws constantly stepped on the toes of the English Captain. She could not know that this was his way of saying, "Here she is! On your ship! Be quick and give me the copper kettle."

After supper, the Captain managed to leave Pocahontas alone for a few moments in the ship's gun room while he handed the copper kettle over to his Indian friend. He was just giving Japazaws' wife a few trinkets for her part in the plot, when Pocahontas came back to join them.

"You are to be our guest on this ship and go with us to James Town, daughter of The Powhatan," the Captain told the girl gently. "We shall not harm you.

A Princess Is Kidnapped

Do not be afraid! You shall be to us as a sister. The price of your freedom is your father's consent to live with us in peace."

The face of the Indian girl did not show the fear she felt in her heart. Women of her tribe were as brave as the men. If tears came to her eyes when she saw Japazaws and his wife leave the boat, she quickly brushed them away.

"Truly, we are your friends, dear Pocahontas, just as you were our friend when Captain John Smith was our leader," Captain Argall comforted the girl on the way down the river.

"You shall be welcomed at James Town as a princess should be. Soon, surely, your father will quickly send for his darling daughter and pay our price for her freedom."

It was as the Captain said. Pocahontas was lodged in one of the best homes in the settlement. The ways of living of the Pale Faces were strange to her at first. But she learned quickly. As the days passed, she understood more and more English words. Soon, she could speak easily with her new friends.

The settlers could not help loving this gay Indian princess. They allowed her to go and come as she liked, so long as she did not try to run away.

But The Powhatan did not send quickly to free his dearest daughter.

In his wigwam at Orapax, far up the Pamunkey, an Indian messenger from James Town told the old Chief of the price which the settlers had set on his daughter's freedom.

"The Long Knives say you must send back the eight English prisoners whom you hold here, Wahunsonacock! You must return the tools, the guns, and the swords which your people have stolen. You must let the Pale Faces buy the corn they now need so badly. And you must promise that there shall forever be peace."

"That my dear daughter is a prisoner makes my heart sad." The old Chief's face was grim. "Tell the Long Knives I beg them to treat Pocahontas with kindness. The eight English prisoners have run away. I shall need time to find them. I shall have to gather in the tools and the guns and the swords from many wigwams. When I can, I will send them."

But it was a full three months before The Powhatan's log canoe came up the river. Then, it brought only seven of the eight Englishmen, a few broken swords, some rusty guns, a broad ax and a saw, and a small heap of corn.

"Give my daughter back to me, and I will fill your barge with corn. You shall then have the rest of your arms and your tools." This was the message that came with the log canoe.

"A promise is not enough." The English governor sent back these words to The Powhatan. "Until our

A Princess Is Kidnapped

price is paid, Pocahontas remains with us here in James Town."

Captain Argall had hoped that The Powhatan himself would come to James Town to seek his dear daughter. But he did not come. And Pocahontas was sad that her father seemed to love her so little.

At last, Sir Thomas Dale, the Governor himself, made ready his river boats with one hundred and fifty men. Captain Argall's vessel, with Pocahontas on board, led the way far up the Pamunkey River to the town where The Powhatan then was encamped.

Four hundred Powhatan warriors were on the river bank at The Powhatan's landing place. They dared the white settlers to set foot on the land. But when the Englishmen boldly came ashore, no bows were drawn, no tomahawks were raised.

"We bring The Powhatan's daughter," the Governor told the warriors. "Bid your weroance come to see for himself that we have treated her well."

But the wary old Powhatan trusted the Englishmen no more than they trusted him. Instead of coming himself, he sent two of his sons.

"My brothers! My dear brothers!" The heart of Pocahontas was joyful to see her own people again. "You can see, I am well. Truly, my friends in James Town have treated me as their own sister."

"We are glad, Little Snow Feather. We had heard

differently. It is good that you are so happy. Our father will rejoice." The young men's dark eyes were bright with their love for their sister.

"Two of our company shall go to The Powhatan!" Sir Thomas Dale ordered. "Master Rolfe and Master Sparkes shall plead with him to make peace with us. And The Powhatan's sons shall remain here until our companions return safely with their father's answer."

Her brothers could not help noticing the loving looks with which Pocahontas watched the two young Englishmen start forth on their errand. Especially fond were her glances after handsome John Rolfe. Later, they learned why her eyes shone so brightly when she spoke this Englishman's name.

Master Rolfe and Master Sparkes did not see The Powhatan. Instead, it was The Powhatan's brother, Opekankano, who spoke with them.

"I will say your words to The Powhatan," Opekankano promised them. "The Powhatan loves his daughter. He, too, wishes peace. No doubt he will soon pay the full price for the freedom of Pocahontas. All yet will be well."

Pocahontas did not seem sad when she heard that her father would not meet the demands of the English Governor. Instead, she smiled as if she were glad to be sailing once more back to James Town.

The Lady Rebekah and Master John Rolfe

"Our Little Snow Feather is happy with the Long Knives," Nantakas told The Powhatan when he and his brother returned from Argall's boat. "They treat her with all kindness. She is content in their homes."

"That is good!" A smile softened the stern face of the old Chief.

"Our sister now knows much of the Englishmen's talk. She wears the clothes of their women. She prays to their God. And they have given her a new name, the English name of Rebekah."

The Powhatan nodded his head with understanding. This did not seem strange to him. His people often gave their children several names. His daughter's secret family name was Matoax, Little Snow Feather. She was Pocahontas to the settlers. Some say she also was called Amonate. It was natural that her new friends should find a name of their own for her.

"But there is something else, Wahunsonacock. This news you will find hard to believe," Nantakas spoke slowly. "Our sister wishes to marry one of the young men of James Town, the young man who is named Master John Rolfe Opekankano has talked with him."

The Powhatan was silent in his surprise. This was hard, indeed, for him to believe. "Who is this John Rolfe? What kind of man is he?" the Chief asked his sons.

"A good man, an honest man, a true gentleman. Everyone says so. Master John Rolfe works hard. He is both wise and kind. He was married before, but his young wife and his baby died of a fever soon after their ship landed at James Town."

"And does this English gentleman also wish for the marriage?" Powhatan was still doubting. It never had happened before in his land that an English gentleman wished to take an Indian girl for his wife.

"The Englishman has sent a letter to the head weroance, Sir Thomas Dale." Nantakas and his brother both remembered how their sister had told them this. "In the letter he tells that he loves Poca-

The Lady Rebekah and Master John Rolfe

hontas as she loves him. He tells that his house is empty and that he is lonely. He wants our sister for his wife because she is so gentle and kind, so pretty to look upon, and so good. He asks the great James Town weroance to grant him permission to make her his wife."

"What does the James Town weroance say?"

"Sir Thomas Dale gladly gives his consent. Now our sister and Master John Rolfe are waiting only until The Powhatan also gives them his blessing."

Like the English Governor, the old Indian Chief was greatly pleased.

"This is sure proof that the Long Knives wish to be our friends," he told his sons. "Little Snow Feather shall marry Master John Rolfe. There shall be peace forever between the Powhatans and the Long Knives."

The bell in the James Town church could be heard far into the forest on the April day when the Lady Rebekah was married to Master John Rolfe. Her English friends decked its wooden walls with gay blossoms. The sweet smells of spring drifted in through its open windows.

A strange throng filled the rows of cedar benches inside the church. It would be hard to say which were the most splendid, the English neighbors of John Rolfe, or the Indian friends of the happy bride.

Sir Thomas Dale and his family were elegant in their colored velvets and satins, and their snowy lace frills. Fifty of the Governor's guardsmen were there, clad in fine scarlet coats.

But the bride's uncle, Opachisco, who represented The Powhatan, and two of the bride's brothers were wearing crowns of red deer hair and eagle feathers. Shining copper links and glistening white shell beads hung round their necks and their wrists. Red puccoon paint colored the cheeks and the shoulders of all the Indian guests. They were dressed in their best.

"A gift for the bride." Sir Thomas Dale put a golden ring on the finger of Pocahontas. It was a handsome gift which had come from the land of Italy, far across the wide waters.

"Our father's gift is here, too," Nantakas said. And he put around his sister's neck a string of gleaming white pearls.

But the best wedding present for the Lady Rebekah and Master John Rolfe was the message which the weroance, Opachisco, delivered in impressive tones:

"The King of the Powhatans speaks through my mouth," Opachisco said. "'I am the friend of the white people.' It is Powhatan himself speaking. 'I am old. I would live forever in peace with the children of King James, from over the sea. My country is large. If need be, I will move my wigwams yet farther away

The Lady Rebekah and Master John Rolfe

from the towns of my white brothers. My warriors shall never attack them again. I, The Powhatan, say it. It shall be so.'"

The wedding guests rejoiced when they heard these words. All looked with love at the pretty young Indian bride in her fine English gown. They thought, "Our dear and blessed Lady Rebekah! Again she has brought us the promise of peace."

Many times after her marriage, the Lady Rebekah begged The Powhatan to visit her. First in her house in James Town, and later in her home on her husband's plantation near the new village of Henrico.

But Powhatan would not come. Often and often he sent her gifts. Always he wanted to hear from his messengers how his dear daughter "lived and loved." Especially did he ask for news of the little son, Thomas, who was born to Pocahontas and Master John Rolfe.

The old Chief never held his English grandson upon his knee. He never saw his dear daughter after her marriage. But to the day of his death in 1618, he kept his promise of peace and friendship for her adopted people.

Those were happy days for the Lady Rebekah and Master John Rolfe. The settlers loved this charming Indian princess, who now lived among them as one of themselves. She had followed their ways. She had learned to call their great river the James, instead of the Powhatan. For her, now, the Pamunkey was the York River. Her father's empire was Virginia. And the great country of which Virginia was part—she, too, called it America.

But the ways of her own people were not entirely forgotten. The things Pocahontas knew so well about the animals and the plants of her land often were of use to her English friends.

John Rolfe was the first of the settlers to make large plantings of the precious tobacco which brought such a high price. On his little plantation near the settlement of Henrico, his wife worked at his side. It was perhaps chiefly because of her that Master John Rolfe's tobacco plantation was such a success.

In the eight years of peace, after the marriage of the Lady Rebekah and Master John Rolfe, the settlements on the James River grew bigger and bigger. More people came across the ocean on every ship.

Men did not need to waste precious time, now, in fighting the Indians. There was peace, thanks to The Powhatan.

The settlers could build better houses, big, fine houses with two floors and an attic. Pocahontas laughed when she first tried out the stairs that led to the upper floor. This was a fine way to climb, she thought.

The Lady Rebekah and Master John Rolfe

The English houses seemed wonderful to her. But, then, so was everything else about her new life.

Each day brought new magic to the Indian girl. Each day, her world seemed more exciting. Each day, she was thankful to the Great Spirit for her husband, John Rolfe, and for Thomas Rolfe, her beloved small son.

A Strange New World

"LAND! Land!" Shouts went up from the sailors on the deck of the ship. Flags were flying gaily atop its three masts. Everyone on board was excited. The long weary journey across the Atlantic Ocean was over.

"England! There is England!" Master John Rolfe and Sir Thomas Dale both pointed to the dark streak on the horizon.

Tears of joy and excitement filled the dark eyes of Pocahontas who stood between them on the deck.

"England! England!" she whispered. She could hardly believe that at last she was to enter that strange and wonderful world across the wide waters.

For so long she had wanted with all her heart to see this land. When she yet was a child, she had begged her "white brother," Captain John Smith, to take her there with him. She had treasured each story of England which her husband had told her at their plantation fireside on winter nights.

The wonders of the great city of London left the girl without words to tell of her feelings. Her eyes opened wide in her amazement at the endless rows of houses, at the many carriages rolling over the cobblestoned streets, and the great crowds of people.

Even more astounded were her two sisters and the other Indians whom The Powhatan had sent to accompany his daughter on this great adventure.

"I shall count the people of this land," one Indian said when he first landed in Plymouth. "On this long stick I shall cut a mark for every person I see. Then I can take a true count back to The Powhatan."

John Rolfe smiled to himself. But he said nothing. It was the Indian who soon grunted with disgust. He threw his stick away, saying, "I shall say to The Powhatan, 'Can you count the stars in the sky? Can you count the leaves in the forest? Or the grains of sand by the sea? Well, no more can you count the people of this England.'"

The greatest surprise for Pocahontas came even before she had reached London. She was at a place called Bradford when her husband announced one day without warning, "A visitor is here. The famous Admiral of New England, Captain John Smith, has come here to see you."

"Dear Lady Rebekah!" John Smith bowed formally over her hand in the courtly English fashion. He must have found it hard to believe that this finely dressed lady was his little Indian friend.

Word had been sent ahead that Master John Rolfe and his Indian Princess were crossing the ocean. John Smith had not waited for their coming to the great city of London. He had made haste to see Pocahontas as soon as ever he learned where she was.

To his surprise and dismay, Pocahontas returned his warm greeting with a cold little bow. Then she turned her head away, and did not speak. The truth was she was hurt at his long years of silence. She remembered how she had grieved for him after the ship took him away from her land to die. She had not known that he had recovered, and that he had made other journeys to America.

There were tears in her dark eyes. She would not look at her old friend. Again and again he begged her to speak to him. But she would not.

"I see I have told our good Queen Anne what is not true," Smith said at last. "I told her the Lady Rebekah could speak our own English language. It must be I was wrong."

Then Pocahontas turned round to face him.

"Do you call me only the 'Lady Rebekah?'" she cried. "Am I then to address you as 'Admiral of New England?' You called The Powhatan 'father' when you

A Strange New World

were a stranger in our land. May I not call you 'father' now that I am a stranger in this land of yours? Am I not still your 'child'?"

"It is that you are the daughter of a great King, Pocahontas," Captain John Smith explained gently. "People here will say I do not show our Indian princess proper respect, if I call her my 'child'!"

"You were not so afraid of people in the Powhatan country." Pocahontas still showed that her feelings were hurt. "There you were the one who made others afraid. You struck fear into the heart of the Great Powhatan and of all of the tribe except me. I tell you I will call you 'father.' You shall call me 'child.' Forever and ever, I shall be of your people.

"They did always say you were dead, my father." Tears again came into her eyes at the memory. "I did not know you still lived until I landed at Plymouth. The Powhatan sought news of you. But the people of James Town did not tell him the truth."

Pocahontas and Captain John Smith had much to say to each other. The Indian girl rejoiced to see her dear friend again. He had not changed. His eyes still were clear and bold. His mustache and his beard were still ruddy gold. His laugh was as merry as when he had played with her at Werowocomico.

Captain John Smith told Pocahontas how he had spread the news of her coming all over London. He spoke of the letter he had sent to Queen Anne, to make sure she would be welcomed at court as a princess should be.

All London knew about this famous letter. It told once more how the little Indian girl had saved the life of Captain John Smith again and yet again. How she risked her own head under the raised tomahawks of her father's warriors! How she came through the forest in the frightening dark to warn him of The Powhatan's plot to take his life! And how she had so often saved the little Virginia settlement from starvation.

"It was only because of The Powhatan's daughter, a prisoner in James Town, that peace at last came to your Majesty's colony in America," Captain John Smith's letter declared. And he begged the Queen and the King to welcome Pocahontas, not as the wife of the English Gentleman, Master John Rolfe, but as the noble daughter of the great Indian King, Powhatan.

The Virginia Princess and her Indian companions were as astonishing to the people of London as that great city was to these visitors. Crowds lined the streets to catch a glimpse of "The Beautiful Savage."

Inns and shops were named in her honor. Noble ladies and gentlemen came to call upon her. Everyone showed her admiration and respect.

A great London artist painted a portrait of The

A Strange New World

Powhatan's daughter in her fine English dress. The tall dark hat she wears in this picture was shaped like a huge acorn, and around it is pictured its costly band of bright gold.

In the English fashion of the day, the Lady Rebekah's scarlet and gold gown was worn with a high ruff and long cuffs of stiff lace. In her hand she carried a fan of curled ostrich feathers, cunningly fastened with bits of glittering mirror.

The artist painted the girl's great, soft eyes, her dark hair, her red lips, and her smooth tawny skin. By the proud tilt of her head, one can easily see she was a person of importance.

At the court all eyes were upon the Lady Rebekah when she was presented to the King and the Queen by Lord and Lady De La Warr. At the balls and the theaters, people scarcely could keep their minds on the entertainments for looking at this princess from America.

Their glances were friendly, however, and the Indian girl never was troubled by the admiring crowds. She delighted in the blaze of colors in the court ballrooms. She enjoyed the gay "masques" that were performed at the theaters. She laughed merrily at their clowns, and she seemed to understand most of the words of the actors who paraded across the stages.

Her favorite was Will Shakespeare's fairy play, "The Tempest." Its woodlands and flying spirits reminded her of her own land. Indeed, there were many things in this strange new world over the sea which were like those at home.

Talk of witches was common in England then. Satan, the English Evil Spirit, was like Okeus, Pocahontas thought. And, of course, the God of the English whom she now worshiped was much the same as her own people's Great Spirit.

The manners of "The Beautiful Savage" were as correct as those of any court lady. Here in England, even at the most splendid banquets, food was lifted to the mouth with the fingers. Knives were for cutting, and spoons were for soups and stews. There were no forks. As in the wigwams of Virginia, bowls of water were passed around for washing hands after meals.

In spite of her pleasure in London and its new adventures, there were moments when Pocahontas could not help feeling homesick. She missed the deep forests of her own land. She longed for the songs of the wild birds and the soft rustle of moving deer. She missed, also, her country's broad rivers, so many times larger than London's small River Thames.

Pocahontas had a place in two different worlds—the world of America and the English world across the Atlantic Ocean. Her days in her husband's land had been exciting. She dearly loved Master John Rolfe and her new friends in England. But she was

Smithsonian Institution

Ætatis suæ 21. Aº. 1616.

Matoaks als Rebecka daughter to the mighty Prince Powhatan Emperour of Attanoughkomouck als Virginia converted and baptized in the Christian faith, and Wife to the Worll Mr Tho: Rolff.

An unknown English artist painted a portrait from life of "The Beautiful Savage" in 1616. (The Booten Hall portrait.)

A Strange New World

glad when it was time to think of sailing back to Chesapeake Bay.

Alas, Pocahontas was never to see her Virginia home again. Before her ship set sail, she became ill. And in 1617, when she was twenty-two years of age, her life was ended. With his mother gone, her little son, Thomas Rolfe, was left behind in the English home of his father's brother.

In both of her worlds, people were sad at the news of the death of The Powhatan's daughter. She loved the two nations to which she belonged. And they both loved her. With her fearless spirit and her loving heart, this Indian girl had been like a bridge between her two worlds. For both England and America she forever will be "the dear and blessed Pocahontas."

Books

about Pocahontas and Her World

IN GATHERING material for this book, the author has consulted many authorities, among which the most helpful have been the following:

Anthropological Papers Nos. 43-48. Smithsonian Bulletin 157, Bureau of American Ethnology. Washington, D. C.: U. S. Government Printing Office, 1955. Contains the original Strachey Vocabulary.

[Archer, Captain Gabriel?]. *A Relatyon of the Discovery of our River,* &c., [1607]. In *Travels and Works of Captain John Smith,* 1608-1631, edited by Edward Arber, I, xl-lv. The English Scholar's Library. Birmingham, 1884.

Brinton, Daniel G. *Myths of the New World.* New York: Leypoldt & Holt, 1868.

Brownell, Charles De Wolfe. *The Indian Races of North and South America.* New York: The American Subscription House, 1859.

Buchanan, James. *Sketches of the History, Manners, and Customs of the North American Indians,* by His Majesty's Consul for the State of New York. New York: W. Borradaile, 1824.

Catlin, George. *North American Indians: Names, Customs, Languages, History, and Conditions.* Philadelphia: Leary, Stuart & Co., 1841.

———. *Life Amongst the Indians.* New York: D. Appleton & Co., 1867.

Cooke, John Esten. *Virginia, History of the People.* Boston: Houghton Mifflin Co., 1883.

Donaldson, Thomas Corwin. *The George Catlin Indian Gallery in the United States National Museum.* Annual Report of the Board of Regents of the Smithsonian Institution, 1885. Washington, D. C.: U. S. Government Printing Office, 1887.

Drake, Samuel G. *The Aboriginal Races of North America.* New York: Hurst & Co.; Philadelphia: C. de Silver, 1860.

Flannery, Regina. *An Analysis of Coastal Algonquian Culture.* Washington, D. C.: Catholic University of America Press, 1939.

Hamor, Ralph, The Younger. *A True Discourse of the Present Estate of Virginia,* [1615]. Albany (New York): J. Munsell, 1860.

Handbook of the American Indians. 2 volumes. Smithsonian Bulletin 30, Bureau of American Ethnology. Washington, D. C.: U. S. Government Printing Office, 1910.

Hariot, Thomas. *A Brief and True Report of the new found land of Virginia* &c., [1588-90]. In Hakluyt's *Voyages,* VI. Everyman's Library. London: J. M. Dent & Sons, Ltd., 1910.

Percy, Master George. *A Discourse of the Plantation of the Southerne Colonie in Virginia,* [1606], from Rev.

Books

Samuel Purchas's *Pilgrimes,* IV, pp. 1685-1690. London, 1625.

Also in *Travels and Works of Captain John Smith,* 1608-1631, edited by Edward Arber, I, lvii-lxxiii.

Smith, Captain John. *Travels and Works of Captain John Smith, President of Virginia, and Admiral of New England,* 1608-1631, edited by Edward Arber. 2 volumes. The English Scholar's Library. Birmingham, 1884.

Includes: *A True Relation of Occurrences and Accidents in Virginia,* [1608].

A Map of Virginia, with a Description of its Commodities, People, Government, and Religion, [1612].

The Generall Historie of Virginia, New England, and the Summer Isles, [1624].

Speck, Frank G. *Ethnology of the Powhatan Tribes of Virginia.* New York: Museum of the American Indian, Heye Foundation, 1925.

Spelman, Henry. *Relation of Virginia,* [1609]. London: Chiswick Press, 1872.

Also in *Travels and Works of Captain John Smith,* 1608-1631, edited by Edward Arber, I, ci-cxiv.

Strachey, William. *History of Travaile into Virginia Britannia,* [1610-15]. London: Hakluyt Society, 1849.

Swanton, John R. *The Indian Tribes of North America.* Smithsonian Bulletin 145, Bureau of American Ethnology. Washington, D. C.: U. S. Government Printing Office, 1952.

Wingfield, E. M. *A Discourse of Virginia,* [1608?]. Boston: J. Wilson & Son, 1860.

Also in *Travels and Works of Captain John Smith,* 1608-1631, edited by Edward Arber, I, lxxiv-xci.

POCAHONTAS AND HER WORLD

* * *

THE AUTHOR wishes to thank Dr. Regina Flannery Herzfeld, Professor of Anthropology of the Catholic University of America, and Dr. William Harlen Gilbert of the Library of Congress, for their kindness in reading the manuscript of this book.

She wishes also to express her gratitude to the Smithsonian Institution for permission to use its photograph of the portrait of Pocahontas.

A NOTE ON THE TYPE
IN WHICH THIS BOOK IS SET

THE TEXT of this book was set on the Linotype in a face called Times Roman, designed by Stanley Morison for *The Times* (London), and first introduced by that newspaper in 1932.

Among typographers and designers of the twentieth century, Stanley Morison has been a strong forming influence, as typographical adviser to the English Monotype Corporation, as a director of two distinguished English publishing houses, and as a writer of sensibility, erudition, and keen practical sense.

GRANT CHRISTIAN SCHOOL
12931   avenue
Grant, Michigan 49327

GRANT CHRISTIAN SCHOOL
12931 Poplar Avenue
Grant, Michigan 49327